A GEOLOGICAL EXCURSION GUIDE TO

THE PALEOCENE IGNEOUS ROCKS OF THE
ISLE OF RUM, INNER HEBRIDES

A GEOLOGICAL EXCURSION GUIDE TO

RUM

THE PALEOCENE IGNEOUS ROCKS OF THE ISLE OF RUM, INNER HEBRIDES

C. H. Emeleus

Department of Earth Sciences, University of Durham, United Kingdom

and

V. R. Troll

Department of Geology, Trinity College, University of Dublin, Éire
Present address: Department of Earth Sciences, University of Uppsala, Sweden

WITH CONTRIBUTIONS BY:

E. P. Holohan

School of Geological Sciences, University College, University of Dublin, Éire

and

G. R. Nicoll

Department of Geology, Trinity College, University of Dublin, Éire

National Museums Scotland

Published in 2008 by
Edinburgh Geological Society

in association with
NMS Enterprises Limited – Publishing
a division of NMS Enterprises Limited
National Museums Scotland
Chambers Street
Edinburgh EH1 1JF

The rights of C. H. Emeleus and V. R. Troll to
be identified as the authors of this book have
been asserted by them in accordance with the
Copyright, Designs and Patents Act 1988.

ISBN: 978 1 905267 22 4

Publication layout and design by
    NMS Enterprises Limited – Publishing.
Cover artwork by Mark Blackadder; photograph
    by V. R. Troll.
Printed and bound in the United Kingdom
    by Cambridge Printing.

For a full listing of titles and related merchan-
dise, please contact:

www.nms.ac.uk/books
www.edinburghgeolsoc.org

Image Credits

*Every attempt has been made to contact
copyright holders. If any images have been
inadvertently missed, please contact the
publishers.*

Figures 8, 13, 25, 43, 45, 49, 54 and 61 are
reproduced with the permission of the
Director, British Geological Survey, © NERC.

Map extracts used as bases for figures 6, 26,
33, 44, 51, 58, 62 and 71 are reproduced with
the permission of Scottish Natural Heritage,
© SNH.

Contents

Acknowledgements

Our understanding of the geology of Rum has profited greatly by many discussions with J. Barraud, J. Bedard, B. R. Bell, G. P. Black, M. H. P. Bott, D. Brown, G. M. Brown, M. Cheadle, C. H. Donaldson, A. C. Dunham, M. Errington, J. Faithfull, M. Forster, A. Fowler, K. Goodenough, J. R. Graham, R. Greenwood, C. J. Hughes, R. H. Hunter, M. Holness, D. Jerram, D. Kitchen, J. McClurg, I. Meighan, G. Nicoll, P. J. Nicholson, B. O'Driscoll, R. Renner, R. Sides, M. Smith, B. G. J. Upton, J. Volker, W. J. Wadsworth and I. M. Young. We are especially grateful to G. Nicoll for help with drafting many of the maps and for providing a number of photographs.

We would also like to thank numerous research and undergraduate students, particularly P. K. Byrne, E. Donoghue, L. McCourt, C. Flanagan and F. Sheehan. D. Stephenson and K. M. Goodenough are thanked for editorial handling of the various versions of this manuscript.

Our work on Rum has been made possible through the help and encouragement of the past and present scientific and estate staff of the Nature Conservancy Council and Scottish Natural Heritage, on and off the island.

Introduction

The Isle of Rum is the largest of the Small Isles in the Inner Hebrides, north-west Scotland (Figure 1). It is a National Nature Reserve, owned and managed by Scottish Natural Heritage (SNH)* and there are several geological Sites of Special Scientific Interest (Emeleus and Gyopari, 1992). In addition to the spectacular geology, the island is noted for its herd of red deer (the subject of a long-term study initated in the 1950s), feral goats, plant life, birds (Rum was used as the base for the reintroduction of the Sea Eagle to the Hebrides), and insects. Rum has a population of about 20, the majority of whom live at Kinloch.

Visitors to Rum can usually freely explore the immediate surroundings of Kinloch, where there are several well-marked nature trails. At certain times during the year there are restrictions on access to parts of the island, especially the northern area around Kilmory which is the centre for ongoing deer studies. Notification of these activities is usually given on the information boards outside the White House. Those walking or working outwith Kinloch should always fill in daily route cards (available outside the White House) and make sure that these are completed on return. Leaders of parties visiting the island must contact the Reserve Manager well in advance of their intended visit; geologists should note that rock sampling can only be carried out with the Reserve Manager's permission. Collecting from loose material is usually not a problem but hammering exposures is not generally permitted.

Rum and the other Small Isles (Eigg, Canna, and Muck) are served by ferry (foot passengers only) from Mallaig, which is connected by road and railway to Fort William (70 km) and Glasgow (240 km), and by road to Inverness (180 km). The nearest airports are at Glasgow and Inverness. There is also a regular vehicle ferry connection (c. 40 minutes) between Mallaig and Armadale on the Isle of Skye.

* SNH, The White House, Kinloch, Isle of Rum, PH43 4RR; Tel. 01687-46-2026; www.snh.org.uk

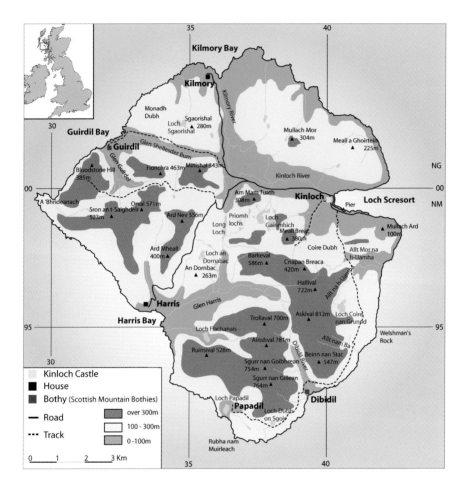

Figure 1. General map of Rum, showing main geographical features.

Fieldwork on Rum generally involves cross-country walking over rough, damp ground and climbing to between 500–800 m elevation. Rain and strong winds are common. It is therefore essential to have good walking boots and adequate waterproof clothing. There is no public transport and all vehicles on the island are for the use of SNH employees. There are no paved roads, only rough tracks and paths.

The island is well known for the ferocity of its midges, which can be very trying on still, humid days. Visitors should bring their preferred repellant and midge nets, for these may not be available on the island. Ticks occur in the areas frequented by

2

deer and goats. The best protection against both of these is provided by long trousers and long-sleeved shirts. There are no snakes on Rum.

A selection of maps and books relating to Rum is listed below. Topographic maps can be obtained through most booksellers or from Edward Stanford Ltd, 12-14 Long Acre, London, WC2E 9LP (www.stanfords.co.uk). SNH publications are available from the Publications Section, Scottish Natural Heritage, Battleby, Redgorton, Perth, PH1 3EW (www.snh.org.uk) and some may be bought from the SNH office on Rum. The SNH 1:20,000 geological map is only obtainable from SNH on Rum. Publications (maps, memoirs, etc.) of the British Geological Survey (www.bgs.ac.uk) can be purchased from: BGS, Murchison House, West Mains Road, Edinburgh, EH9 3LE; BGS Keyworth, Nottingham, NG12 5GG; The Natural History Museum, Earth Sciences Galleries, South Kensington, London; or through approved stockists. (NB: BGS publications required for educational purposes and ordered through an educational establishment may attract a discount.)

Maps

Visitors to Rum should bring a copy of the Ordnance Survey 1:25,000 map and use this at all times when in the field.

Ordnance Survey topographic maps:
   1:50,000 Landranger series: Sheet 33, *Rum and Eigg*
   1:25,000 Explorer series: Sheet 397,
   Rum, Eigg, Muck, Canna and Sanday

Geological maps
1:50,000 British Geological Survey Scotland Sheet 60, *Rum*
   (Solid & Drift) (1994)
1:20,000 Scottish Natural Heritage, *Rum – Solid Geology*
   (Second Edition, 1992) (obtainable only from SNH on Rum)

Selected books, etc.

GOODENOUGH, K. and BRADWELL, T. (2004): *Rum and the Small Isles: A Landscape fashioned by Geology* (Redgorton, Perth: Scottish Natural Heritage).

BELL, B. R. and WILLIAMSON, I. T. (2002): 'Chapter 14: Tertiary igneous activity', in TREWIN, N. H. (editor): *The Geology of Scotland* (London: The Geological Society).

EMELEUS, C. H. (1997): 'Geology of Rum and the adjacent islands', *Memoir of the British Geological Survey*, sheet 60 (Scotland) (Nottingham: British Geological Survey).

EMELEUS, C. H. and BELL, B. R. (2005): *British regional geology: the Palaeogene volcanic districts of Scotland* (fourth edition) (Nottingham: British Geological Survey).

UPTON, B. G. J. (2004): *Volcanoes and the Making of Scotland* (Edinburgh: Dunedin Academic Press).

Travel

Caledonian MacBrayne operates a service from Mallaig to Rum and the other Small Isles. Details about the current timetable and fares should be obtained from Caledonian MacBrayne (Mallaig 01687-46-2403; or see the company's website, www.calmac.co.uk). For train connections between Mallaig, Fort William and Glasgow, consult the National Rail Timetable or First Scotrail (www.firstgroup.com/scotrail). Buses operate between Mallaig and Fort William (Shiel Buses, Acharacle, Argyll, PH36 4JY; shiel.buses@virgin.net). As ferry departures from Mallaig are generally earlier than the arrival of trains (except on Saturdays during the summer), it is necessary to stay in Mallaig overnight. Hotel, B&B and other accommodation is available but should be booked in advance. A summer ferry service also operates between Arisaig and Rum on certain days; for details contact Arisaig Marine (tel. 01687-465224; www.greentourism.org.uk/ArisaigMarine). Private vehicles (cars, motorcycles, etc.) are not permitted on the island and the SNH office on Rum should be consulted about the use of mountain bikes prior to arrival.

NB: Ferry sailings can be delayed or cancelled when there are adverse weather conditions. This rarely happens during the summer and delays are less frequent since the completion of the new slipways on Rum and the other islands.

Accommodation

Accommodation (self-catering/individual meals/full board) is currently available at Kinloch Castle hostel (contact: The Manager, Kinloch Castle, Isle of Rum, PH43 4RR, Tel. 01687-46-2037). Camping is allowed at Kinloch; elsewhere camping is strictly controlled and may only be arranged with the permission of the Reserve Manager. Bothies maintained by the Scottish Mountain Bothies Association are located at Dibidil [NM 393 927] and Guirdil [NG 320 013]; the Reserve Manager should be consulted if it is intended to use these.

A small licensed shop and post office next to the community hall [NM 403 997] at Kinloch sells a selection of groceries and beverages. Opening hours are from about 17.00–19.00. A limited selection of postcards may be available and postcards may also be on sale in the castle, along with Scottish Natural Heritage literature about Rum. A comprehensive selection of SNH publications about Rum is obtainable from the Reserve Office which is open on mornings, Monday–Friday. There is a public telephone near the old post office [NM 403 996] and in the castle courtyard. At present, mobile phone reception is possible on parts of the east side of the island, but is poor to non-existent elsewhere.

Items needed for the bothies

The bothy accommodation is spartan. There are two rooms, each of which has a fireplace, a table, and some benches. There is no plumbing and at Dibidil there is no nearby source of fuel (driftwood or otherwise). If you wish to light a fire in this bothy, bring a supply of fuel (kindling, firewood, coal, firelighters, matches, etc.). Sleeping bags, cooking utensils, a lightweight stove, all food, and candles/torches will be required. Mobile phone signal is generally good in the Dibidil bothy.

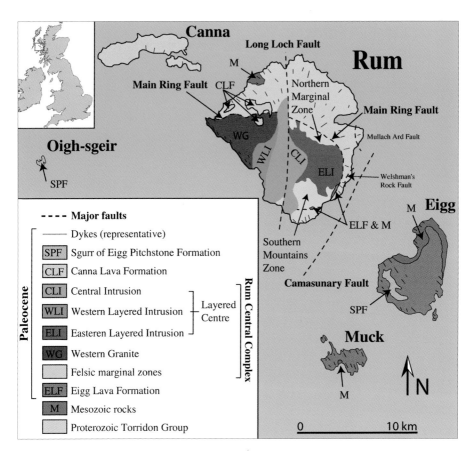

Figure 2. Simplified geological map of Rum and adjacent islands.

Summary of the Geology of Rum

The Paleocene Rum Central Complex (*c.* 60 Ma; Figure 2) is situated on a ridge composed of Archaean Lewisian gneisses and sandstones belonging to the Late-Proterozoic Torridon Group. The ridge is bounded to the east and west by basins filled with Mesozoic sedimentary rocks and Paleocene basalt lavas. On Rum, Torridon Group sandstones form the country rocks to the Paleocene central complex. Numerous north-west- to north-trending, predominantly basaltic dykes of Paleocene age traverse these sandstones, which are overlain in north-west Rum by Triassic sandstones and Paleocene lavas and conglomerates. Relict masses of Paleocene basaltic lavas, Jurassic sedimentary rocks, Torridon Group sandstones, and Archaean gneisses crop out within the central complex. The geological succession is summarised in Table 1 (page 8).

The Rum Central Complex developed in two distinct stages. During **Stage 1**, central uplift on a major arcuate fault system (the Main Ring Fault, MRF) was accompanied by felsic and mixed felsic/mafic magmatism and the formation of a caldera which filled with silicic ash flows, tuffs, and breccias formed by collapse of the uplifted dome and the unstable caldera walls. The country rocks were strongly domed over the central complex, probably accompanied by contemporaneous lateral displacement of large masses of sandstone, while uplift within the ring faults brought masses of Lewisian gneiss and the basal members of the Torridon Group close to the present erosional levels, with later subsidence resulting in the preservation of Jurassic sedimentary rocks and Paleocene basaltic lavas. Slightly later, several microgranites were intruded, including the Western Granite.

7

Table 1: Sequence of faulting, folding and intrusion in the Rum Central Complex

1. Pre-Palaeogene: tilt to west of Triassic and Torridonian strata; faulting in these successions; early movement on the Long Loch Fault?

2. Doming of the Torridonian strata around the central complex accompanied initial uplift, with formation of the Welshman's Rock and Mullach Ard faults as country rocks slid off the dome. Fault blocks broke up and behaved independently, the Welshman's Rock block rotating *c*.90°.

3. Initial uplift on the Main Ring Fault (MRF): Lewisian and basal Torridonian uplifted by as much as 2 km, also tilting of elevated block to the east.

4. Subsidence on the MRF: eruption of rhyodacite ash flows, intrusion of rhyodacite along the MRF, intrusion of tuffisites, collapse of caldera walls to form breccias and mega-breccias, intrusion of the Am Màm Breccias; subsidence brings Broadford Beds and Eigg Lava Formation flows down *c*.1 km within the MRF.

5. Emplacement of the Western Granite (may have been associated with movement that formed the inner component of the MRF).

6. Final uplift on the MRF (inner component).

7. Emplacement of radial dykes, regional north-west-trending dykes, and cone sheets.

8. Formation of a Loch Scresort–Glen Shellesder Fault?

9. Emplacement of the Eastern and Western layered intrusions.

10. Emplacement of the Central Intrusion – re-activation of the Long Loch Fault?

11. Small radial faults within the Central Intrusion and Eastern layered intrusion.

12. Accumulation of the Canna Lava Formation (Skye Lava Group), with concomitant erosion of the Rum Central Complex.

13. Long Loch Fault (final movement); faults in Canna Lava Formation.

Table 1. Major geological events on Rum.

Stage 2 commenced with the intrusion of a set of basaltic cone-sheets and numerous basaltic dykes, many of which trend north-west to north-north-west and belong to the Rum Dyke-swarm. Emplacement of the Rum Layered Centre (feldspathic peridotites, troctolites and gabbros) followed. On Hallival and Askival, in eastern Rum, these mafic and ultrabasic rocks form prominent, gently-dipping layers (generally termed 'Units') and comprise the Eastern Layered Intrusion (formerly 'Series'). Layered rocks also occur in south-west Rum where they form the Western Layered Intrusion. The Central Intrusion separates the Western and Eastern layered intrusions. This comprises a north–south belt of igneous breccias composed of blocks and megablocks of bytownite troctolite and feldspathic peridotite enclosed in matrices of similar compositions. The Central Intrusion is regarded as the feeder system for the Layered Centre. It is located along a major north–south fracture, the Long Loch Fault. Numerous sheets and plugs of gabbro and feldspathic peridotite intrude the layered rocks, and they are also found as plugs throughout the country rocks. A few dykes, including rare picrites, also intrude the Layered Centre.

After Stage 2: a major volcanic edifice was likely built over Rum during stages 1 and 2, but subsequent (and probably also contemporaneous) erosion rapidly reduced this to a hilly landscape. Evidence for this comes from north-west Rum where the Western Granite and sandstones of the Torridon Group are overlain by predominantly basaltic lava flows and intercalated fluviatile conglomerates, belonging to the Canna Lava Formation (c.60 Ma). The flows and conglomerates have buried and preserved a hilly landscape dissected by steep-sided valleys that drained central Rum. The interlava conglomerates contain abundant clasts of red sandstone and gneiss, together with rhyodacite, microgranite, troctolite and gabbro, all clearly derived from the central complex. Clasts derived from Rum have also been identified in conglomerates belonging to the Canna Lava Formation on Canna and Sanday (Emeleus, 1973) and in conglomerates interbedded with lavas belonging to the Skye Lava Group in south-west Skye. Since the Skye lavas pre-date the earliest gabbros of the Paleocene Cuillin Centre on Skye (59 Ma), the Rum Central Complex (60.5 Ma) was clearly extinct and thoroughly dissected before intrusion of the earliest members of the Skye Central Complex.

There is a gap in the geological record from the Paleocene until the Pleistocene Epoch, when the island was almost completely covered by the Main Late Devensian ice sheet sourced in mainland Scotland. At a later stage, during the Loch Lomond Stadial, it supported a local ice cap with several valley glaciers. The ice had gone by about 11,500 BP and there is evidence that Man arrived fairly soon thereafter; at Kinloch a recently excavated site yielded implements made from the bloodstone found in the lavas of north-west Rum. Remains from this site have been dated at about 8,500 BP.

Pre-Paleocene Geology

Lewisian Gneiss Complex

Archaean gneisses crop out along and within the Main Ring Fault (Figure 2; Tilley 1944; Bailey, 1945, 1956). They include interbanded felsic and mafic varieties and amphibolites after original mafic dyke or sheet intrusions. The outcrops are generally fault-bounded or cut by later intrusions but at a few localities gneiss is unconformably overlain by coarse-grained sandstone at the base of the local Torridonian succession; for example, in Sandy Corrie [NM 374 940], and near the Priomh-lochs [NM 370 986]. The gneisses have been thermally metamorphosed to varying degrees and felsic varieties may show signs of partial melting (e.g. Holness and Isherwood, 2003).

Torridon Group

The group is part of the more extensive Torridonian succession found on the mainland and is represented on Rum by a succession of sandstones, siltstones and, locally, sedimentary breccias totalling at least 2500 m in thickness, and several of the mainland formations are recognised (Figure 3). The rocks are largely unmetamorphosed, except in the vicinity of the central complex and adjacent to plugs and other minor intrusions (e.g. Holness and Isherwood, 2003). The group is best developed in the north of Rum where the beds dip consistently west to west-north-west at 10° to 30°, giving rise to the pronounced terrace featuring seen, for example, on Monadh Dubh (Figure 11); however, where affected by doming in the vicinity of the Main Ring Fault, the dips are commonly steep (Excursions 1 and 2).

Medium- to fine-grained feldspathic sandstones of the Applecross Formation form most of the Torridon Group succession on Rum. This formation lacks good marker horizons but members of other formations have distinctive lithologies that have proved to be of considerable use in elucidating the structure of Rum. They are the dark-coloured, fine-grained siltstones of the Laimhrig Shale Member (TCDL), the coarse-grained gritty sandstones of the Fiachanis Gritty Sandstone Member (TCDF) and the fine-grained sandstones and siltstones of the topmost Sgorr Mhòr Sandstone Member (TCSM), characterised by the presence of dark grey to black beds rich in heavy minerals (principally magnetite, but also zircon, garnet, sphene and rare green tourmaline) (Figure 3). The rocks of the Torridon

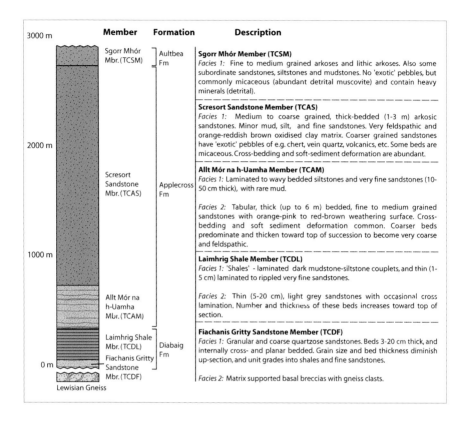

3000 m	Member	Formation	Description

Sgorr Mhór Member (TCSM)
Facies 1: Fine to medium grained arkoses and lithic arkoses. Also some subordinate sandstones, siltstones and mudstones. No 'exotic' pebbles, but commonly micaceous (abundant detrital muscovite) and contain heavy minerals (detrital).

Scresort Sandstone Member (TCAS)
Facies 1: Medium to coarse grained, thick-bedded (1-3 m) arkosic sandstones. Minor mud, silt, and fine sandstones. Very feldspathic and orange-reddish brown oxidised clay matrix. Coarser grained sandstones have 'exotic' pebbles of e.g. chert, vein quartz, volcanics, etc. Some beds are micaceous. Cross-bedding and soft-sediment deformation are abundant.

Allt Mór na h-Uamha Member (TCAM)
Facies 1: Laminated to wavy bedded siltstones and very fine sandstones (10-50 cm thick), with rare mud.

Facies 2: Tabular, thick (up to 6 m) bedded, fine to medium grained sandstones with orange-pink to red-brown weathering surface. Cross-bedding and soft sediment deformation common. Coarser beds predominate and thicken toward top of succession to become very coarse and feldspathic.

Laimhrig Shale Member (TCDL)
Facies 1: 'Shales' - laminated dark mudstone-siltstone couplets, and thin (1-5 cm) laminated to rippled very fine sandstones.

Facies 2: Thin (5-20 cm), light grey sandstones with occasional cross lamination. Number and thickness of these beds increases toward top of section.

Fiachanis Gritty Sandstone Member (TCDF)
Facies 1: Granular and coarse quartzose sandstones. Beds 3-20 cm thick, and internally cross- and planar bedded. Grain size and bed thickness diminish up-section, and unit grades into shales and fine sandstones.

Facies 2: Matrix supported basal breccias with gneiss clasts.

Group on Rum are considered to have been laid down within a major fluvial braidplain (Nicholson, 1992, 1993).

Figure 3. Stratigraphy of the Torridon Group on Rum (after Nicholson, 1992).

Mesozoic strata

Sedimentary breccias, gritty sandstones and calcareous sandstones and siltstones of the Triassic Monadh Dubh Sandstone Formation crop out in small outliers in north-west Rum. Cornstones (caliches) are present and are particularly conspicuous at the angular unconformity with the Torridon Group rocks (Excursion 6). Rare ostracods and ill-preserved plant remains occur in the uppermost beds (Bailey, 1945; Steel, 1974, 1977; Emeleus, 1997). The Triassic rocks of Rum are

11

probably the feather-edge of the Mesozoic Minch Basin (Binns *et al.*, 1974; Fyfe *et al.*, 1993).

Coarse-grained grey marble, calc-silicate hornfelses, quartzite and baked mudstones crop out south of Allt nam Bà and on the northern slopes of Dibidil. Poorly preserved fossils of Early Jurassic age have been recovered from these rocks which are correlated with the Broadford Beds of Skye (Smith, 1985). These beds are preserved in fault-bounded slices on the Main Ring Fault. At Allt nam Bà, where they are in contact with Marginal Gabbro of the central complex, the hornfelsed rocks contain the calc-silicate minerals spurrite, tilleyite and harkerite, indicating high-grade sanidinite-facies thermal metamorphism (Excursion 7; Hughes, 1960b; Emeleus, 1997).

Paleocene

Pre-Stage 1

Basaltic lavas belonging to the Eigg Lava Formation probably covered much of Rum prior to initiation of Stage 1 of the central complex. These lavas are now restricted to faulted slivers of basalt within the Main Ring Fault in eastern Rum. Additionally, locally abundant xenoliths of basic granulite-facies hornfels ('beerbachites') up to 10 m long occur in ultrabasic rocks in the Eastern Layered Intrusion (Stage 2). They are considered to be foundered blocks derived from lavas that roofed the central complex (Excursion 3). Clots and veins in the xenoliths contain grossular, calcic plagioclase and iron-rich pyroxene (ferri-fassaite), possibly derived from the metamorphism of lava amygdales (Faithfull, 1985).

It is likely that some of the numerous north-west- to west-north-west-trending basaltic dykes that intrude the Torridonian beds pre-date the central complex since these and less common sheets are affected by movements on the Main Ring Fault. However, conclusive proof is elusive and the majority of the dykes on Rum probably belong to the early part of Stage 2 (see below).

THE RUM CENTRAL COMPLEX

Stage 1

THE AM MÀM BRECCIAS

Evidence for some of the earliest activity within the central complex comes from the Am Màm Breccias in the Northern Marginal Zone (Table 1, page 8; Excursion 2). The breccias consist of abundant angular blocks in dioritic to granodioritic matrices, with textural relationships that suggest there has been mixing of felsic and mafic magmas. The xenoliths are commonly less than 1 m across but may be many metres in width. They comprise angular blocks of very coarse-grained gabbro, dolerite, rare feldspathic peridotite, baked sandstone and gneiss, and, additionally, there are small (up to 10 cm) rounded doleritic inclusions with diffuse margins. Areas of very coarse-grained gabbro several tens of metres in diameter are identical to gabbro fragments in the breccias. Gabbros east and west of Am Màm hill are cut by veins and more substantial bodies of breccia and maintain their coarse-grained character throughout, generally lacking any indications of chilled margins except at one locality east of Loch Gainmhich where gabbro grades into finer grained rocks at a contact with thermally metamorphosed Lewisian gneiss (pyroxene hornfels). These large areas of gabbro were previously considered to be plugs (e.g. Dunham, 1968) but are now interpreted to be megablocks in the Am Màm Breccia. Similar igneous breccias are present in the Southern Mountains Zone.

THE COIRE DUBH BRECCIAS

Coarse sedimentary breccias feature prominently in both the Southern Mountains Zone (SMZ) and their type locality, the Northern Marginal Zone (NMZ), where they crop out abundantly in Coire Dubh, between Meall Breac and Cnapan Breaca (Excursion 2; Figure 4a). In the NMZ, the breccias consist of angular to subrounded blocks of sandstone and siltstone derived from the lowermost members of the Torridon Group, principally the Fiachanis Gritty Sandstone. Gneiss and dolerite clasts occur but are extremely rare in the NMZ. The breccias may be clast- or matrix-supported, the matrix commonly consisting of comminuted sandstone. The fragments vary in diameter from a few centimetres to over a metre and, at several localities, large rafts, or 'megablocks', of bedded sandstone appear

13

Figure 4. Panoramic views of the Northern Marginal Zone and Southern Mountains Zone:

a. Coire Dubh area with Cnapan Breaca and Hallival, viewed from the north-west. Rocks of the Northern Marginal Zone form the low foreground (Coire Dubh Breccia) and the pale crags and exposures on Cnapan Breaca (centre; rhyodacite ash flows). The base of the crags on Cnapan Breaca marks the position of bedded tuffs and fine-grained sandstone. The Marginal Gabbro of the Eastern Layered Intrusion forms the grassy area on the right-hand

flank of Cnapan Breaca, and the terraced slopes leading up to Hallival mark the positions of 'allivalite' (bytownite troctolite) in layered units in this intrusion.

b. Dibidil river valley. Rhyodacite ignimbrite sheets and sedimentary breccias make up the back wall of Nameless Corrie and the ridge to Ainshval on the left of the photograph. Layered units in the Eastern Layered Intrusion form the distinctive peak of Trollaval in the far centre. Faulted Lewisian gneisses and Torridonian sandstones crop out along the foreshore to the right.

to be enclosed by breccia, although in the absence of complete exposure it may be difficult to prove this interpretation. The clearest apparent examples of megablocks occur in the Southern Mountains Zone (SMZ, Excursion 8; Figure 4b) but they are probably also present in the NMZ (Excursion 2). The Coire Dubh Breccias are commonly chaotic, but locally display bedding, and stratigraphical successions have been established in both areas (Figures 15 and 70) (e.g. Troll *et al.*, 2000; Donaldson *et al.*, 2001). Tuffs, including crystal tuffs rich in plagioclase similar to that found in later porphyritic rhyodacite, occur in the breccias, with good examples to the east and north of Cnapan Breaca (Excursion 2). Coarse, pale grey, gritty sandstone is generally present at the top of the breccias. This sandstone, the Epiclastic Sandstone, formed when fines washed out of the breccias accumulated in areas of shallow water on the caldera floor (Excursions 2 and 7).

Despite their close proximity on the south side of Am Màm (at *c.* [NM 3817 9853]), the relative age of the Am Màm and Coire Dubh breccias is difficult to establish with certainty. However, on the north side of Meall Breac and in the SMZ there is evidence that the Am Màm Breccias were closely associated with porphyritic rhyodacite (Excursions 2 and 8).

The two breccias are of very different origins. The Am Màm Breccia is intrusive and has a thoroughly igneous matrix with the characteristics of a hybrid (mixed felsic/mafic) magma, whereas the Coire Dubh Breccia formed from debris that accumulated against the walls and on the floor of a caldera (Emeleus, 1997; Troll *et al.*, 2000; Donaldson *et al.*, 2001).

PORPHYRITIC RHYODACITE

Large bodies of porphyritic rhyodacite (the 'porphyritic felsite' of Hughes, 1960a and Dunham, 1968) crop out in both the NMZ and the SMZ (Figures 4, 6). The resistant rock forms Cnapan Breaca, Meall Breac and Am Màm in the NMZ (Excursion 2; Figure 4a), and Sgurr nan Gillean and Ainshval in the SMZ (Figure 4b). The porphyritic rhyodacite contains variable amounts (20–50 vol. %) of phenocrysts of bipyramidal quartz, complexly-zoned plagioclase, opaque oxides and iron-rich pyroxenes (ferro-augite, ferropigeonite and Fe-rich hypersthene). The matrices vary from microcrystalline (devitrified glass) to fine-grained granular aggregates of quartz, plagioclase, alkali feldspar and amphibole. Rounded, lobate mafic enclaves occur in the rhyodacite. The inclusions are commonly

15

several tens of centimetres in diameter and are abundant locally in both zones, as towards the north end of Meall Breac and in a major plug of rhyodacite north of Cnapan Breaca (Excursion 2, Locality 5). Rhyodacite of both intrusive and extrusive origins is exposed in the walls of corries on the south-west side of Dibidil; mafic enclaves are abundant at some localities (Excursion 8). The relationships in both areas are indicative of a mixed-magma origin for the rhyodacites (Troll *et al.*, 2004).

Streaky, banded structures in the rhyodacite (fiamme) occur on both outcrop and microscopic scales (Excursion 2). The banding was formerly attributed to the flow of viscous, degassed felsic magmas, but it is now recognised that the structures closely resemble fiamme and, in the devitrified glassy matrices, relict shards are readily recognised. Additionally, phenocrysts are commonly broken, and small, rounded pieces of basalt (< 1 cm diameter) are scattered throughout the rock. The rocks are now interpreted to be pyroclastic flow deposits that erupted from vents on or near the Main Ring Fault and accumulated on the floor of a caldera (Williams, 1985; Donaldson *et al.*, 2001). On Meall Breac, a flow feeder at the north end of the ridge has close-set, near-vertical banding (highly-attenuated fiamme) and may be traced southwards into a thick, extrusive mass of rhyodacite overlying the Coire Dubh Breccia. Nearby, on a shelf north of Meall Breac, a dyke-like mass of porphyritic rhyodacite cuts the Am Màm Breccia (Excursion 2). A few small intrusive bodies of porphyritic rhyodacite crop out on the Main Ring Fault and on the south-east slopes of Beinn nan Stac and in Coire Dubh.

TUFFISITES

Irregular, thin (< 30 cm), dark-coloured dykes cut sandstones and the Coire Dubh Breccia in Coire Dubh and Dibidil. The dykes are generally xenolith-rich, with abundant small fragments of country rock and rare, bleb-like pieces of porphyritic rhyodacite. Microscopic examination shows the presence of rounded mafic inclusions with a fluidal structure, banded rhyodacite, altered basalt and dolerite, and crystals of quartz and zoned plagioclase similar to those in the rhyodacite. The dykes are examples of tuffisites. They either just pre-date the rhyodacite or are contemporaneous with it, and may represent the earliest rhyodacite magma cracking through to the surface, although this remains speculative (Excursions 2, 7 and 8).

MICROGRANITES

The hills and coastal cliffs of west and south-west Rum are formed by the Western Granite, an intrusion of granophyric microgranite. Other small areas of microgranite occur near the Priomh-lochs (the Long Loch Granite) and on the south-west of Sgurr nan Gillean (the Papadil Granite, Excursion 9). The rocks are pale-brown or cream coloured, with small feldspar phenocrysts and drusy cavities visible on weathered surfaces. The phenocrysts are zoned plagioclase and the matrix is commonly micro-granitic or of granophyrically intergrown quartz and dusty alkali feldspar. Pyroxenes (ferroaugite and ferropigeonite) are the principal mafic minerals, although both show varying degrees of replacement by amphibole and chlorite. A pale-weathering, cream-coloured variant of the granite near Harris contains fayalitic olivine and ferrohedenbergite. This may be a later member and, elsewhere, internal contacts have been noted.

The northern margin of the Western Granite is defined by the later Main Ring Fault. In the east, it is cut by mafic rocks belonging to Stage 2. Original intrusive contacts are limited to a small patch of thermally altered gneiss on the summit of Ard Nev and a strip of gneiss between the microgranite and feldspathic peridotite between Ard Nev and Ard Mheall. To the north-west, on Orval, lava flows belonging to the Canna Lava Formation rest on an irregular eroded surface of weathered microgranite (Excursion 5). Else-where, the Papadil Granite (Excursion 9) appears to cut porphyritic rhyodacite (Hughes, 1960a) and breccias of Am Màm type, indicating that the microgranites are probably the youngest members of Stage 1.

The Main Ring Fault

The Main Ring Fault comprises a number of arcuate faults that define the outer margins of Stage 1 and were probably utilised in part during emplace-ment of Stage 2 (Figures 2, 9). The faults may be traced from A' Bhrìdeanach in western Rum along the northern edge of the central complex to Cnapan Breaca (e.g. Figure 6), then south to Allt nam Bà and Dibidil, and west to Papadil where they are truncated by Stage 2 intrusions. Between Cnapan Breaca and Beinn nan Stac the margin of the later Eastern Layered Intrusion roughly coincides with, and is presumed to have been controlled by, the Main Ring Fault. Other mafic intrusions belonging to the Layered Centre breach the ring fault between Minishal and the Long Loch Fault, and north-east of the Priomh-lochs.

Movement on the Main Ring Fault was complex. The earliest events are most clearly visible on the northern edge of the NMZ and in the vicinity of Allt nam Bà and Beinn nan Stac. Here, Lewisian gneiss and basal members of the Torridon Group occur exclusively inside the ring fault, demonstrating that considerable uplift (as much as 2 km) has occurred within this fault system. For example, in Allt Slugan a'Choilich in Coire Dubh, sandstones from the Applecross Formation and dark siltstones from the stratigraphically lower, Laimhrig Shale Member are in juxtaposition (Excursion 2). A more complicated situation exists on the south-east slopes of Beinn nan Stac, where the Main Ring Fault (MRF) comprises Inner, Central and Outer branches (Excursion 7; Smith, 1985). In an east to west traverse the following are encountered (Figure 8): (i) Applecross Formation sandstone faulted against gneiss (Outer MRF); (ii) gneiss faulted against basalts of the Eigg Lava Formation overlying Lower Jurassic Broadford Beds (Central MRF); and (iii) Broadford Beds faulted against gritty sandstones and siltstones of the Diabaig Formation (Inner MRF). These relationships are interpreted to show initial uplift of > 1.5 km on the Outer MRF, followed by subsidence (> 1 km) on the Central MRF and caldera formation, and a final phase of uplift (> 1 km) on the Inner MRF.

Throughout most of its length the Main Ring Fault appears to be either essentially vertical or steeply inclined towards the central complex. Inward-dipping components of the system occur on the eastern slopes of Beinn nan Stac, and between the Bealach a' Bhràigh Bhig south of Fionchra and the western tip of Rum at A' Bhrìdeanach.

In eastern Rum several large masses of Torridonian strata have also been displaced along low-angle faults. The most obvious of these blocks is the steeply-dipping mass of sandstone (Applecross Formation) that forms Welshman's Rock. At Lochan Dubh, gently-dipping sandstone to the west is separated from the block by the clearly-defined Welshman's Rock Fault, which is inclined to the east at about 35°. Another mass of sandstones belonging to the Applecross Formation overlies a low-angled, easterly inclined fault at Mullach Ard on the south side of Loch Scresort. The dip of the sandstones is largly undisturbed, but the rocks are faulted against siltstones of the Laimhrig Shale Formation, and Nicholson (in Emeleus, 1997) estimated that a minimum downward displacement of 500 m accompanied by lateral movement towards the east-north-east is necessary to explain the present disposition of these rocks. The exact age of the movement on these two faults is difficult to determine but they post-date some of the minor intrusions, since crushed dolerite sheets crop out next to both faults. These blocks are interpreted to have slid off a dome that developed as felsic magmas ascended during Stage 1 of the central complex.

The southern tip of Rum, from Rubha nam Meirleach to the Main Ring Fault on the south of Sgurr nan Gillean, is formed by sandstones of the Sgorr Mhòr Sandstone Member and uppermost Scresort Sandstone Member at the top of the Torridon Group on Rum. Prominent dark beds rich in heavy minerals, characteristic of the Sgorr Mhòr Member, are magnificently exposed in the sea cliffs east of Papadil. When the position of these strata is compared with those in northern Rum, it is clear that this southern block has undergone considerable normal downward displacement. Some of the movement may be attributable to displacement on the Long Loch Fault, although this could only have been very limited (see below). The most likely explanation is that this large block also slid off the dome that developed over the central complex during Stage 1. Significantly, the beds in this block are cut by the MRF to the east of Papadil.

Minor intrusions: the commencement of Stage 2

Minor intrusions are abundant on Rum. Dykes are the most common, but there are also numerous plugs and cone-sheets, and less-common conformable sheets and sills. Almost all of the dykes are basaltic in composition. They generally lack distinctive characteristics in the field, although 'big-feldspar' and picritic varieties are readily recognisable. Dykes generally range in width from 0.2 m to 1.5 m. Over forty gabbro and peridotite plugs have been mapped, varying in size from 20 m up to 500 m. These are particularly abundant in the sandstones in the north and north-west of Rum and appear to radiate from the central complex (Excursion 6). The gabbros are generally olivine free and may be considerably altered. The peridotite plugs include feldspathic varieties and rare dunites. Bleaching and thermal metamorphism of the adjoining sandstones is common and is especially pronounced next to the gabbroic intrusions where some partial melting of country rocks has occurred (e.g. Holness, 1999).

The majority of the minor basaltic intrusions probably post-date both the Main Ring Fault and Stage 1 (but see Excursion 7). The cone-sheets are apparently unaffected by the Main Ring Fault, for example north-west of Am Màm, and they post-date deformation of the Torridon Group rocks adjoining the NMZ. In south-east Rum many north-west-trending dykes belonging to the regional swarm extend into the SMZ where they and the cone-sheets intrude porphyritic rhyodacite and earlier rocks (Emeleus, 1997; Excursions 7, 8, 9). However, several thick dolerite dykes on the lower south-east slopes of Beinn nan Stac probably pre-date Stage 1 since they are not found within the Outer MRF. A few north-west- to north-trending dolerite dykes intrude flows belonging to the Canna Lava Formation. They are distinct from the large number of north-west-trending dykes on the north-west coast of Rum, which are part of the Rum Swarm and do not cut the lavas. The post-Canna Lava Formation dykes also differ from the majority of igneous rocks on Rum in that several exhibit normal remnant magnetisation whereas most others are reversely magnetised (Dagley and Mussett, 1981).

Conformable basaltic sheets intrude members of the Torridon Group outside the Main Ring Fault. At least three different types may be distinguished. Sheets up to 3 m in thickness crop out in two areas. Those south-west of Kilmory are characterised by plagioclase and clinopyroxene phenocrysts, whereas those north-east of Papadil are aphyric (Excursion 9). Much thinner sheets of aphyric basalt (0.5 m and less) occur in both the northern and southern sandstone tracts. They are less common in the sandstones of eastern Rum, but examples of probable pre-Stage 1 age sills are cut by the Welshman's Rock and Mullach Ard faults.

It is difficult to determine when the plugs were intruded since few cut or are cut by dykes and none can be shown to be faulted. Gabbro and peridotite plugs do, however, cut the Main Ring Fault (e.g. near the Priomh-lochs; Excursion 2) and the Layered Centre (e.g. on Cnapan Breaca [Excursion 2] and Beinn nan Stac) and some of the plugs are amongst the latest intrusions in Stage 2. The elongate peridotite plugs in north-west Rum have a radiating pattern and appear to fan out from the Long Loch area, the possible site of the major feeder of the Layered Centre (see below). They frequently exert significant thermal influence on their immediate surroundings, e.g. Torridonian sandstone lithologies (cf. Holness, 1999, 2002).

Stage 2: The Layered Centre (formerly the 'Layered Suite')

Intrusions of feldspathic peridotite, bytownite troctolite (allivalite) and gabbro form the core of the Rum Central Complex. Three divisions, formerly termed 'series', are recognised: the *Eastern Layered Intrusion*

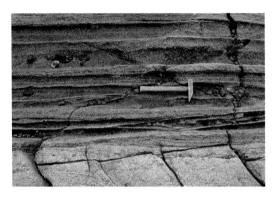

Figure 5. Intricate layering in troctolites (allivalites), showing sedimentary-style features in the Central Intrusion. Locality 4.4, west of the Long Loch, central Rum. Scale: hammer shaft 30 cm.

(ELI), the *Western Layered Intrusion* (WLI), and the *Central Intrusion* (CI) (Figures 2 and 6).

THE EASTERN LAYERED INTRUSION (ELI)

The layered character of mafic rocks in the Layered Centre is most apparent in this intrusion in which a succession of gently dipping sheets of peridotite, allivalite and gabbro are magnificently exposed on Askival, Trollaval, Hallival and Barkeval (Figures 5, 6).

Up to sixteen layered units have been recognised (Figure 31). Ideally, a unit contains a basal feldspathic peridotite which passes upwards into troctolite (formerly 'allivalite') and anorthositic troctolite, with individual units separated by thin chromite-rich layers. The units were originally envisaged to have crystallised from discrete pulses of basaltic magma. Initially, dense magnesian olivine settled under gravity to form a basal peridotite. This was joined by increasing amounts of anorthite-rich plagioclase to make troctolite and, in some instances, anorthosite. Gabbroic facies with significant clinopyroxene occur towards the top of certain units. Currents disturbed the crystallising magma from time to time, accounting for the ubiquitous small-scale layering and accentuating plagioclase orientation (lamination) in the troctolites (Brown, 1956; Wager and Brown, 1968; Figure 5; Excursion 3). The peridotites and gabbros are classic examples of igneous cumulates (Wager *et al.*, 1960). The units formed an upward-growing succession. Semiconcordant sheets of gabbro intruded the layered units, for example on the Askival Plateau (Brown, 1956; Excursion 3) and in the walls of Atlantic Corrie.

21

Figure 6. Geological map draped over topography. Oblique view from the northwest (© Crown copyright/database right 2004; an Ordnance Survey/[Datacentre] supplied service. Courtesy of J. Barraud). The central complex is separated from the Torridonian country rock by a topographic shoulder that is also a geological boundary marking the Main Ring Fault. Note the pink and orange colours of Stage 1 rocks (rhyodacites and micro-granites) being underlain and intruded by the ultrabasic rocks of Stage 2. Post-central complex igneous activity is marked by strong erosion and deposition of lavas of the Canna Lava Formation on the Western Granite and the MRF. (See pp. 148-49 for full key; based on SNH 1:20,000 solid geology map; © SNH.)

These interpretations were subsequently shown to be somewhat simplistic (e.g. Bedard *et al.*, 1988; Renner and Palacz, 1987). Several sheets of feldspathic peridotite intrude troctolite (Excursion 3) and there are instances of apparent intrusive behaviour by bytownite gabbro ('eucrite') that had been mapped as parts of units (Holness, 2005). Many of the layered rocks do, however, contain structures simulating those found in clastic sedimentary rocks. Of these, the most obvious is the layering, analogous to sedimentary bedding but in which the 'beds' generally reflect differences in modal mineralogy rather than grain size. Others include slump and load structures and rare cross-bedding (Figure 5). There is ongoing controversy about the origins of the structures. Some regard them as primary features related to crystal sedimentation in the magma chamber; others consider that they resulted from interaction between original cumulates

22

and later magmatic fluids generated, for example, from (or by) intruding peridotites (cf. Bedard *et al.*, 1988; Volker and Upton, 1990, 1991; Emeleus, 1997 and references therein; Holness, 2005; O'Driscoll *et al.*, 2007b). Structures resembling those found in highly deformed and sheared metamorphic rocks are also present, occurring especially in the more feldspathic troctolites. These distinctive rocks may have resulted from mass flow of poorly consolidated crystal mushes. Good examples are found in Units 13 and 14 close to the path on the north-west shoulder of Hallival (Excursion 3). The layered rocks represent the crystallised products of high-temperature magmas that cooled and consolidated over an appreciable time span; it is therefore most likely that early-formed structures and textures will have been modified and overprinted by later events, some of which were likely analogous to diagenesis in sediments. Present investigations are gradually unravelling these complex events (e.g. Holness, 2005; Holness *et al.*, 2005; Holness, 2007; Holness *et al.*, 2007a, b; O'Driscoll *et al.*, 2007a, b).

THE WESTERN LAYERED INTRUSION (WLI)

This intrusion is largely composed of layered feldspathic peridotite, underlain by layered gabbro at Harris Bay (Wadsworth, 1961; Excursion 4b). The large-scale layering common throughout the ELI is less obvious in the WLI but small-scale layering is well developed and usually reflects variations in the proportions of olivine and plagioclase, sometimes accompanied by size variation and crystal lamination. In an unusual variety of layering, commonly up to 1 m in thickness, elongate crystals of olivine tens of centimetres in length appear to have grown upwards from a substrate of granular olivine, giving rise to 'harrisitic' textures (Figure 7, Excursion 4b). Good examples may be examined on the benches and low cliffs near the Harris Bay mausoleum, where harrisitic layers extend to within a metre or less of the edge of the intrusion (Excursion 4b). Excellent examples also occur on the southern slopes of Ard Nev and in exposures east of Ard Nev where small harrisitic olivines are present in layered peridotites, which also contain laminated layers with abundant platy olivine apparently broken off the tips of harrisitic olivines. The harrisitic olivines are considered to have grown rapidly from a fast-cooling magma supersaturated in olivine (e.g. Donaldson, 1974, 1976; O'Driscoll *et al.*, 2007a).

23

THE CENTRAL INTRUSION (CI)

This intrusion intrudes both the Eastern and Western layered intrusions (Figure 6), cutting a north–south swathe through them from the Long Loch to Papadil (Figure 2). Although layered peridotites and troctolites are present, the intrusion is characterised by igneous breccias (Donaldson, 1973). The breccias occur in approximately north–south zones, tens to hundreds of metres in width, in which angular to subangular blocks and megablocks of peridotite and troctolite are embedded in predominantly feldspathic peridotite matrices (Volker and Upton, 1990). The troctolite clasts commonly display layering, which dips steeply in all directions although generally remaining fairly uniform in direction within a clast. Large or small individual clasts may record complex events involving crystal sedimentation, or the disruption and/or replacement of layered structures. In turn, layered structures in the enclosing peridotite record considerable disturbance and disruption, commonly suggesting that clasts and blocks subsided into incompetent surroundings, probably crystal mushes (Excursion 4). Elsewhere, layered structures may appear slumped, or disturbed by avalanches of 'pebbly' peridotite debris and by dropstones (Excursion 4). Much of the debris within the breccias resembles fragments of peridotite and troctolite from the earlier intrusions. West and south of the Long Loch, large rafts of troctolite are many tens of metres in extent. These megablocks have steeply dipping layering and were probably derived from the ELI. Layered structures are especially well developed in the troctolites and feldspathic peridotite exposed in the CI west of the Long Loch

Figure 7. Harrisitic olivines in the Central Intrusion. Individual crystals may reach over 60 cm in length. See text for details.

where slump structures, graded bedding, flame structures and other features suggesting 'soft sediment' deformation are much in evidence (Excursion 4). On the western slopes of Trollaval there is a progressive increase of dip in the ELI units when traced westwards, indicating that at some stage substantial masses of layered rocks sagged towards the Central Intrusion and probably broke off and subsided into it (cf. Figures 6, 43; Volker and Upton, 1990; Emeleus *et al.*, 1996; O'Driscoll *et al.*, 2007b).

A distinctive structure is found in feldspathic peridotites north-east of Loch MacIver (Loch an Dornabac). Radiating, bifurcating crystals of plagioclase up to 40 cm in length, enclosing myriads of minute olivine crystals, occur in seaweed-like masses as much as 1 m in diameter, scattered through the normal feldspathic peridotite. These 'poikilo-macro-spherulitic' feldspars grew *in situ*, possibly from a hydrous feldspathic magma (Excursion 4; Donaldson *et al.*, 1973). Other cases of *in-situ* crystallisation are apparent in the CI and around Harris where radiating crystals of olivine reach lengths of up to several tens of centimetres (cf. Figure 7).

During the original survey of Rum (Harker, 1908), many instances were found where the peridotites, troctolites and gabbros in the Layered Centre had been intruded by 'granophyre' (microgranite) and 'felsite' (porphyritic rhyodacite) from which it was concluded that the felsic rocks were the younger. At first sight the field evidence seems incontrovertible: wherever the mafic rocks are in contact with felsic rocks, there are spectacular breccias in which angular to subrounded mafic rocks are embedded in a network of veins and dykes of fine- to medium-grained microgranite that merge into the adjoining felsic rocks (Excursion 4). Many years later this interpretation was challenged and it is now known that the breccias are intrusion breccias, formed when hot mafic magmas chilled against but also melted or partially melted silicic country rocks. These were principally microgranite and porphyritic rhyodacite, but also sandstones and felds-pathic gneisses (Hughes *et al.*, 1957; Hughes, 1960a; Emeleus, 1997). The relatively low-temperature, rheomorphic felsic melts had burst through and fragmented the chilled and contracting margins of the mafic intrusions, producing (rare) sinuous, rounded liquid-liquid contacts where still-liquid mafic magma chilled against the relatively low-temperature felsic liquids, while in some instances, hybrid rocks were formed when heated felsic magma was able to mingle with mafic magma. Thus, the rocks of the Layered Centre clearly post-date the felsic rocks of Stage 1 (Figures 6, 8). Additional supporting evidence comes from the minor intrusions; basaltic

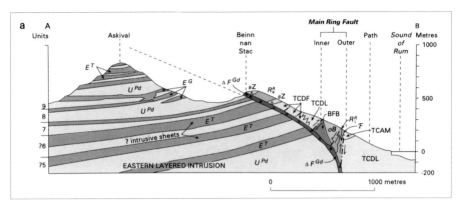

Figure 8. Cross-section through the south-east portion of the Rum Central Complex (Askival – Beinn nan Stac – Sound of Rum), illustrating relationships and tectonics along the Main Ring Fault system, after Emeleus (1997) (see pp. 148-49 for full key.) (© NERC)

dykes and cone-sheets, which intrude the porphyritic rhyodacite, micro-granite and feldspathic sandstones of the Torridon Group, can be followed into the contact zone where they underwent progressive thermal meta-morphism and veining by thin silicic stringers. Ultimately, the dykes could no longer be supported by their weakened, partially melted felsic surrounding, whereupon they collapsed and disintegrated, contributing to the mafic blocks in the intrusion breccias. Some of the best examples come from fragmented cone-sheets in upper Dibidil (Hughes, 1960a) but convincing exposures may be examined in the contact zones at the south end of Meall Breac and Cnapan Breaca, at the ELI contact about 3 km east of Hallival, and at the WLI margin at the east end of Harris Bay (Excursions 2, 4b).

The scenario outlined above provides an explanation for the absence of good chilled margins to the constituents of the Layered Centre; they were simply destroyed during formation of the intrusion breccias (but see Greenwood et al., 1990). The problem is a general one throughout the Hebridean Igneous Province so that the most promising localities to search for good chills (possibly representing rapidly cooled parental magma) are at gabbro/basalt lava contacts, which are lacking on Rum. The problem of the parental magma or magmas of the Layered Centre has exercised investiga-tors since the original survey (e.g. Harker, 1908; Brown, 1956; Emeleus, 1997 and references therein), with the present consensus favouring a magnesium-rich basalt, possibly most closely represented by rare picritic dykes that post-date the Layered Centre (Upton et al., 2002).

The Canna Lava Formation on Rum

Several small outliers of lava flows with interbedded conglomerates and gritty sandstones crop out on the hills of north-west Rum. These belong to the Canna Lava Formation that is part of the Skye Lava Group (Table 1, p. 8). Four members have been distinguished using field and chemical criteria: the Lower Fionchra Member (conglomerates with rare plant remains; flows of olivine basalt and hawaiite), the Upper Fionchra Member (conglomerate; gritty sandstone and siltstone with plant remains; flows of tholeiitic basaltic andesite with hyaloclastite deposits at the base), the Guirdil Member (conglomerate; flows of tholeiitic andesite ['icelandite'] and the Orval Member (flows of olivine-bearing basaltic hawaiite and hawaiite).

These lavas post-date the Rum Central Complex. This is in marked contrast to central complexes elsewhere in the Hebridean Igneous Province where the lava successions are almost invariably intruded by the central complexes. Conclusive evidence for their younger age emerged when Black (1952) excavated the contact between lava flows and microgranite on Orval. He found that the lavas rest on a surface of weathered microgranite (Excursion 5). Further evidence is provided by the clasts in the conglomerates. These include boulders, cobbles and pebbles of porphyritic rhyodacite, microgranite, gabbro, troctolite and tuffisite derived from the central complex, together with feldspathic sandstone, gneisses and amphibolite. The lavas and conglomerates have strikingly irregular outcrops (Figures 6, 58; Excursions 5 and 6), partly due to faulting but largely the result of their burying a succession of irregular palaeolandscapes. Consecutive members have infilled valleys excavated in pre-lava rocks and also in earlier flows, as on Bloodstone Hill and Fionchra (Excursion 5). The valleys were generally floored by coarse conglomerates, in places interbedded with gritty sandstones and sandstones. On Fionchra a basaltic andesite hyaloclastite breccia overlies plant-bearing siltstones, implying that from time to time the valleys may have contained shallow lakes. Plant remains have been recovered from these beds (Jolley, 1997). Since no lava feeders are known on Rum, the flows are assumed to have originated from external sources, ponding in valleys carved into the flanks of the Rum central volcano (Emeleus, 1985). Apart from a few basaltic dykes that intrude the lavas, the lava flows represent the latest igneous activity on the island.

Accumulation of the Canna Lava Formation overlapped with the unroofing of the Rum Central Complex and occurred within a short time span. An age of 60.53 ± 0.08 Ma (Hamilton *et al.*, 1998) has been obtained from the Layered Centre (Stage 2), which is very similar to dates from the Canna Lava Formation on Canna (60.00 ± 0.23 Ma; Chambers *et al.*, 2005) and the Skye Lava Group on Skye (58.91 ± 0.1 Ma). The earliest intrusion in the Cuillin Centre of the Skye Central Complex intrudes lavas of the Skye Lava Group and has been dated at 58.91 ± 0.08 Ma (Chambers *et al.*, 2005; Emeleus and Bell, 2005 and references therein). Thus, little over one million years separate the Rum and Skye central complexes which, in turn, bracket a period of intense erosion and lava effusion (e.g. Williamson and Bell, 1994).

Events post-dating the Rum Central Complex

THE LONG LOCH FAULT

This fault extends in a general north–south direction across Rum (Figures 2, 6), producing up to 800 m of right-lateral displacement of rocks that include the latest members of the Central Intrusion. It is not possible to estimate the amount and direction of any vertical displacement, but it is unlikely that there can have been a significant downthrow to the east. Had this occurred, members of the Canna Lava Formation would likely have been preserved to the east of the fault. Within the central complex, the fault follows the course of the Central Intrusion where it is marked by a shallow, steep-sided valley up to 50 m in width (Excursion 4). However, to the north the valley is noticeably wider in Kilmory Glen, where there is evidence that the zone of faulting is appreciably wider than within the central complex. It is suggested that the Long Loch Fault was already active prior to emplacement of the central complex, becoming re-activated during the Paleocene when it acted as a conduit for the mafic magmas of the Layered Centre (and probably earlier intrusions in the central complex; O'Driscoll *et al.*, 2007b), and hence probably for most of those erupted during Stage 2 (McClurg, 1982; Emeleus *et al.*, 1996).

Numerous small faults occur throughout Rum. Some may be relatively early, as for example the north-east-trending fault that affects Torridonian beds on Bloodstone Hill but which is overlain by lavas. Others are of later date, as at West Minishal where lavas and conglomerates are cut by a north-north-west-trending fault that also offsets the MRF. Small, north-north-west- to north-north-east-trending faults also offset layering in the ELI north of Barkeval.

THE PLEISTOCENE AND LATER

Rum was much affected by the Pleistocene glaciations and retains a record extending from at least 30,000 BP to the Holocene (Peacock, in Emeleus, 1997). The Main Late Devensian Glaciation enveloped Rum, when only the highest peaks formed nunataks. From the distribution of glacial striae and mainland erratics (mica schist and garnetiferous gneiss), which occur at heights of over 500 m on Barkeval and Ard Nev, it is concluded that the mainland ice sheet covered much of Rum except where diverted by local ice centred on the highest peaks. Prominent rock benches and sea cliffs are a feature of the western Rum coastline between Harris and A' Bhrìdeanach (Excursion 4b) and are present also in eastern Rum, north and south of Loch Scresort. The benches formed when sea level was appreciably higher than at present. In places they are covered by glacial deposits and they are therefore considered to be of pre-Late Devensian age. Other shoreline features of later date were formed during the Windermere (Late-glacial) Interstadial (c.14,700 BP). These include the small raised-beach deposits near Guirdil and those backing bays between Loch Scresort and Kilmory. The most spectacular deposits dating from this time are the raised storm beaches at Harris Bay (Excursion 4b). Rum was the centre of a local glaciation during the Loch Lomond Stadial (c.13,000 BP). Numerous small corrie glaciers filled the valleys and clung to the hillsides, leaving moraines and hummocky till deposits.

Man inhabited Rum from an early date, and discovered bloodstone, a green-coloured chalcedonic form of silica with flecks of red, oxidised pyrite. The bloodstone, which is found in fissures and cavities in flows of the Upper Fionchra Member of the Canna Lava Formation, was brought from Bloodstone Hill to a site at Kinloch where numerous fragments have been recovered from a site and dated at about 8,500 BP (Wickham-Jones and Woodman, 1998). During the nineteenth century there was a fashion for items of jewellery made from bloodstone and the Rum deposits were worked once more. However, because of their precarious situation high on the cliffs at Bloodstone Hill, the workings were completely closed off. The best present-day source of bloodstone, and small banded agates, is in the beach gravels close to the Guirdil bothy.

Excursions on Rum

The approximate areas covered by each excursion are indicated on Figure 9. Remember that Rum is a National Nature Reserve and prior permission must be obtained from SNH if you need to collect rock samples. Consult the Reserve Manager if in any doubt. As far as possible samples should come from loose material (of which there is usually an abundance).

Figure 9. Map of Rum showing the location of each excursion as a box.

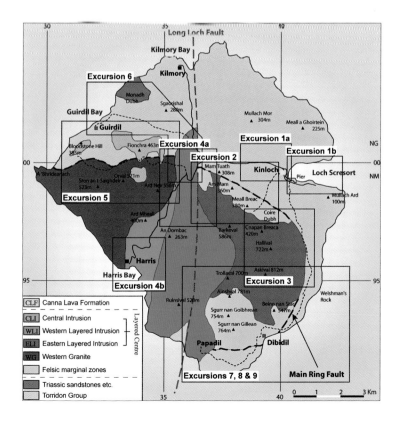

31

Excursion 1
Kinloch and surroundings

HIGHLIGHTS

Minor basic and ultrabasic intrusions will be seen on the first part of the excursion, with spectacular metamorphism of the country rocks. The distinctive topography associated with the Torridon Group in north Rum is well displayed, as are the disturbed Torridonian rocks along the northern margin of the central complex. The Applecross Formation (Torridon Group), intruded by Paleocene dykes, is excellently displayed in coastal exposures east of Kinloch, traversed in the second half of the excursion, and there is evidence for a major fault affecting the Torridon Group rocks.

The boat from Mallaig normally reaches Rum before 2 pm, except on summer Saturdays when the early service arrives at about 9 am. The first afternoon may be spent around Kinloch, on the sandstones of the Torridon Group and the numerous Paleocene minor intrusions. The latter include basaltic sheets and dykes, and several plugs of feldspathic peridotite and gabbro (Figures 10, 12). Alternatively, if time on Rum is limited, some or all of the localities in Coire Dubh could be visited (Excursion 2; Figure 13; Localities 2.1 to 2.8).

(A) West of Kinloch

Take the Kilmory road west from Kinloch, along Kinloch Glen (Figure 10). Sandstones belonging to the Scresort Sandstone Member of the Applecross Formation (TCAS) in the Torridon Group crop out in the adjacent Kinloch River and in roadside exposures. They have a general dip of 15–20° to the west-north-west. These sandstones occur on either side of the glen and cause the strong features on Mullach Mòr to the north (Figure 11).

Locality 1.1 [NM 3927 9987]

Kinloch Glen – sandstone intruded by dolerite plug and sheet

About 1 km from Kinloch a small dolerite plug and a south-dipping dolerite sheet are exposed in the roadside. Sandstone near the dolerite is somewhat bleached and has developed numerous irregular joints, both of which are features typically found near the numerous small doleritic and gabbroic intrusions in northern Rum.

Pass through the deer fence (close the gate) and continue along the track for 900 m, noting several north-trending dykes and exposures of dolerite (plugs).

Locality 1.2 [NM 3803 9983]

Bridge over Allt Bealach Mhic Neill – peridotite plug in sandstone

At the bridge over the Allt Bealach Mhic Neill there are exposures of brown weathering peridotite belonging to a plug more than 200 m wide.

Figure 10. Map of Excursion 1A, west of Kinloch (see pp. 148-49 for full key).

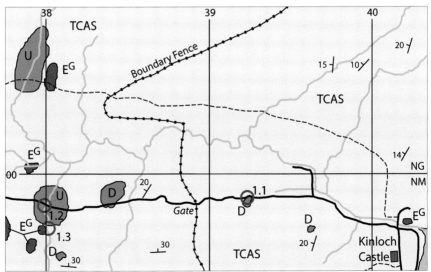

33

Figure 11. Regular west-north-west-dipping Torridonian sandstone beds on Mullach Mòr, with the Skye Cuillin in the distance.

Locality 1.3 [NM 3803 9966]

Allt Bealach Mhic Neill – spectacular spherulithic structures in baked sandstone adjoining gabbro plug

Follow the path on the eastern (right-hand) side of the Allt Bealach Mhic Neill for about 250 m south, to the foot of a waterfall. The feldspathic sandstone (TCAS) in the stream bed has a spectacular spherulitic texture (Holness, 2002). The sandstone has been extensively recrystallised and partially melted by the gabbro plug seen in the left-hand stream bank. It contains quartz paramorphs after tridymite and relict quartz grains in a fine-grained felsic matrix. The alteration is considered to have occurred at a depth of about 700 m (Holness, 2002). Return to the bridge (Locality 1.2). On the north side of Kinloch Glen, the uniformly west-dipping sandstones on Mullach Mòr are seen to be interrupted by a wide cleft at [NG 379 005]. This is the site of a peridotite plug, with a small gabbro plug on its eastern margin. Turning towards the south and south-west, many slab-like outcrops are visible on the hillside. One large slab, about 300 m to the west-south-west of the bridge, is formed by a gabbro plug [NM 379 997], but the majority are of sandstone that dips steeply (60° or more) to the north. They are part of a belt of steeply dipping strata that extends along the north side of the central complex, from A'Bhrìdeanach [NM 298 995] in western Rum to the hillsides south of Kinloch. The beds became tilted as doming developed over the central complex during the rise of felsic magmas in Stage 1. Return to Kinloch. (Total distance c. 2.5 km.)

(B) South side of Loch Scresort

From Kinloch Castle go to the White House (the SNH Reserve Office) and take the shore road. Cross a small stream and go down to a rocky promontory immediately to the north-east (Figure 12).

Locality 1.4 [NM 4044 9928]

White House, Kinloch – picrite dyke cutting sandstone

Sandstone on the promontory is cut by a broad, north-east-trending picritic dolerite dyke with abundant fresh olivine

Figure 12. Map of Excursion 1B, east of Kinloch (see pp. 148-49 for full key).

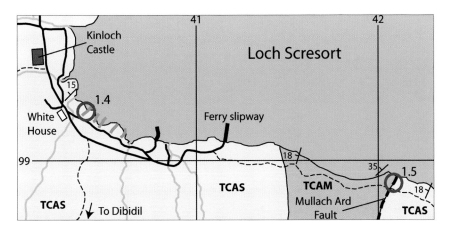

crystals. This dyke is probably the continuation of the picritic dolerite that cuts Stage 1 rocks in Allt Slugan a'Choilich in Coire Dubh (Excursion 2; Locality 2.2). Continue east past the new ferry terminal (c. 1 km east of the White House) and take the path along the south side of the loch. West-north-west-dipping sandstone belonging to the Scresort Sandstone Member is cut by several thin north-east- to north-north-east-trending basalt dykes and less common south-dipping basalt sheets. Some 400 m east of the ferry terminal, coarse-grained sandstones of the Scresort Sandstone Member (TCAS) give way to progressively finer grained beds down the sequence that make up the Allt Mòr na h-Uamha Member (TCAM) (Figure 3).

Locality 1.5 [NM 4208 9893]

Cro nan Laogh – Torridonian sandstone displaced along the low-angle Mullach Ard Fault

At Cro nan Laogh, cyclically interbedded siltstones and sandstones in the Allt Mòr na h-Uamha Member are well exposed and a thin (50 cm) basalt sheet is intruded near the base of the cliff. Immediately to the east, coarse-grained sandstones belonging to the Scresort Sandstone Member are downfaulted against the finer grained beds by the Mullach Ard Fault. This fault extends south to Bàgh na h-Uamha [NM 423 974] and is inclined at c. 35° in an easterly direction. It is one of several low-angle faults in eastern and southern Rum on which substantial masses of country rocks are thought to have slid off the central complex when a dome-like structure developed early in Stage 1. Return to Kinloch. (Total distance c. 4 km.)

Excursion 2

The Northern Marginal Zone (NMZ)

Coire Dubh – Meall Breac – Am Màm – Priomh-lochs area

HIGHLIGHTS

This excursion will examine the rocks of Stage 1 exposed in Coire Dubh and on the low hills south of Kinloch (Cnapan Breaca, Meall Breac and Am Màm). The traverse, from Kinloch into Coire Dubh to the south, crosses *in-situ* Torridon Group rocks to the Main Ring Fault, then caldera breccias, rhyodacite ash flows and small intrusions of rhyodacite (with evidence of mixing of basaltic and rhyodacitic magmas). On Am Màm, a distinctive intrusive breccia is seen to pre-date intrusive rhyodacite. Further west, near the Priomh-lochs, Archaean gneisses are overlain by coarse sandstone belonging to the Fiachanis Gritty Sandstone Member (Torridon Group).

The distance for this excursion is about 10 to 15 km, depending on options chosen, and the highest point reached is nearly 350 m (Figure 13). Leave Kinloch by the path from the castle along the west bank of Allt Slugan a'Choilich. Once clear of the trees around Kinloch, sandstone belonging to the Scresort Sandstone Member is encountered, intruded by numerous south-west-dipping sheets of aphyric to sparsely feldspar-phyric basalt that form part of a cone-sheet swarm (Figure 14). Representatives of the swarm are well exposed in the bed of Allt Slugan a'Choilich, particularly above the altitude of 150 m where the resistant basalt sheets form a succession of small waterfalls. Follow the path or stream uphill towards Coire Dubh, noting the increased north to north-north-west dips of the sandstones.

37

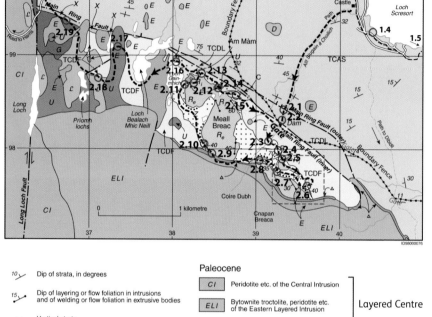

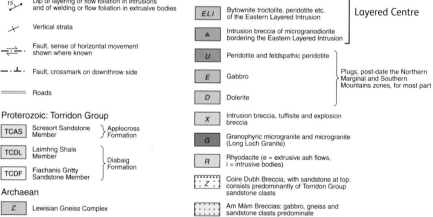

10↙	Dip of strata, in degrees
15↙	Dip of layering or flow foliation in intrusions and of welding or flow foliation in extrusive bodies
✗	Vertical strata
⇄	Fault, sense of horizontal movement shown where known
—·—⊥—	Fault, crossmark on downthrow side
===	Roads

Proterozoic: Torridon Group

TCAS	Scresort Sandstone Member	} Applecross Formation
TCDL	Laimhrig Shale Member	} Diabaig Formation
TCDF	Fiachanis Gritty Sandstone Member	}

Archaean

ℒ	Lewisian Gneiss Complex

Paleocene

CI	Peridotite etc. of the Central Intrusion	
ELI	Bytownite troctolite, peridotite etc. of the Eastern Layered Intrusion	Layered Centre
△	Intrusion breccia of microgranodiorite bordering the Eastern Layered Intrusion	
U	Peridotite and feldspathic peridotite	
E	Gabbro	Plugs, post-date the Northern Marginal and Southern Mountains zones, for most part
D	Dolerite	
X	Intrusion breccia, tuffisite and explosion breccia	
G	Granophyric microgranite and microgranite (Long Loch Granite)	
R	Rhyodacite (e = extrusive ash flows, i = intrusive bodies)	
Z	Coire Dubh Breccia, with sandstone at top: consists predominantly of Torridon Group sandstone clasts	
	Am Màm Breccias: gabbro, gneiss and sandstone clasts predominate	

Figure 13. Geological map of Excursion 2: the Northern Marginal Zone. Dykes and cone-sheets omitted. Modified after Emeleus and Bell (2005). (©NERC)

Locality 2.1 [NM 3935 9835]

Allt Slugan a'Choilich – steeply dipping, indurated mudstone within
strands of Main Ring Fault

At a point where the path is close to the stream, water-worn slabs expose
black mudstone cut by thin (< 1 m) basalt cone-sheets (Figure 14). The
mudstone, which dips steeply to the north, belongs to the Laimhrig Shale
Member (TCDL) and is thought to have been uplifted between the outer
and inner components of the Main Ring Fault (Figure 13). Brecciation and
extensive quartz veining can be observed locally.

Locality 2.2 [NM 3932 9828]

Allt Slugan a'Choilich – Inner Main Ring Fault

At 195 m altitude, a small dam diverts Allt Slugan a'Choilich into the
Kinloch hydro-electric pipeline. Sandstone (TCDF) exposed in the path about
40 m north of the dam appears spotted, due to thermal metamorphism.

Figure 14. Cone-sheet intruding Torridonian
sandstone, Allt Slugan a'Choilich, beside the
Coire Dubh path. Scale: hammer shaft 30 cm.

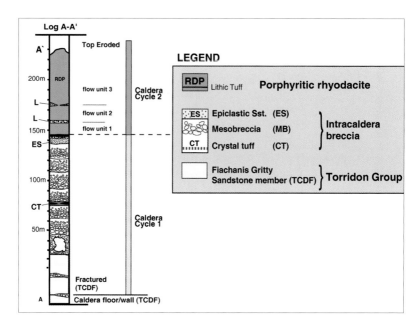

Figure 15. Stratigraphical column of the Coire Dubh intra-caldera succession (simplified after Troll *et al.,* 2000).

Between the dam and the deer fence, a zone of crushed and sheared sandstone and siltstone marks the position of the inner Main Ring Fault. Inclined sheets are abundant in the stream below this point, but are virtually absent at higher levels, inside the inner fault. Upstream from the dam, the stream has eroded a steep-sided gorge along a north-north-east-trending fault and a later picrite dyke that cuts the Main Ring Fault.

Pass through the deer fence (close the gate) into Coire Dubh. Steeply dipping, current-bedded coarse sandstone (the Fiachanis Gritty Sandstone Member, TCDF) is exposed along the path for about 150 m. This is the lowermost member of the Torridon Group on Rum, and its presence indicates further uplift, this time within the inner Main Ring Fault. Note that the Torridonian beds are folded into a tight anticline that strikes approximately west-north-west and is cross-cut by the inner Main Ring Fault (Dunham and Emeleus, 1967).

Figure 16. Coire Dubh Breccias in Coire Dubh: chaotic assemblage of angular and subangular clasts mainly derived from the Fiachanis Gritty Sandstone Member of the Diabaig Formation. Scale: yellow tape-measure is 8 cm diameter.

Figure 17. Tuffisite dyke intruding Coire Dubh Breccias, Coire Dubh. Scale: tape-measure opened to 13 cm.

Figure 18. Mixed-magma plug of rhyodacite with numerous basaltic to andesitic enclaves. Locality 2.3, north of Cnapan Breaca.

Locality 2.3 [NM 3917 9807]

Coire Dubh – basal Coire Dubh Breccia, with incipient fracturing in nearby sandstone

The boundary between slightly shattered sandstone and the Coire Dubh Breccia is seen close to the east bank of the stream, at 300 m altitude (cross the stream with caution). This spectacular breccia consists of angular and subrounded fragments of gritty sandstone, sandstone, siltstone and indurated mudstone derived from the lowest members of the Torridon Group (TCDF, TCDL). The clasts are generally from 1 cm to over 30 cm in diameter and are in a matrix of finely comminuted sandstone and siltstone. Rare clasts of dolerite, basalt and gneiss occur, but the breccia consists essentially of Torridonian lithologies (Figures 15, 16).

Locality 2.4 [NM 3927 9794]

Coire Dubh – tuffisite dyke cutting Coire Dubh Breccia

Follow the contact east and south-east for about 200 m to where it is cut by a 1 m-thick tuffisite dyke with fragments of sandstone and rhyodacite porphyry in a dark matrix (Figure 17).

Locality 2.5 [NM 393 979]

Coire Dubh – 'mixed-magma': rhyodacite plug with mafic enclaves

A short distance to the east, a porphyritic rhyodacite plug intrudes the breccias (Figure 18). The rhyodacite contains abundant mafic enclaves and sandstone fragments. The former commonly show bulbous liquid-liquid contacts at outcrop and in thin section, representing a classic 'mixed magma' occurence (Troll *et al.*, 2004). Continue uphill for 300 m in a south-east direction to the remains of a lochan [NM 3960 9763], in a shallow basin at 365 m altitude.

Locality 2.6 [NM 396 976] (Figure 19)

Cnapan Breaca – bedded breccias, sandstone and rhyodacite ash flows

The base of the Coire Dubh Breccias is exposed on the slopes south-east of the silted-up lochan where thinly bedded tuffs, including crystal tuffs and tuffs with coated lapilli, are interbedded with a much attenuated thickness of coarse breccias that extend to the south (Locality 2.6a). 150 m south of the lochan, extrusive porphyritic rhyodacite with streaky, variably attenuated fiamme, dipping south-west at 40–45°, overlies weakly bedded tuffs, which in turn overlie a thin, impersistent bed of epiclastic sandstone (Z^{SA} on Figure 19; Figure 20). Thin tuffs also occur within the rhyodacite close to its base (Locality 2.6b [NM 3955 9752]). To the south, the rhyodacites end

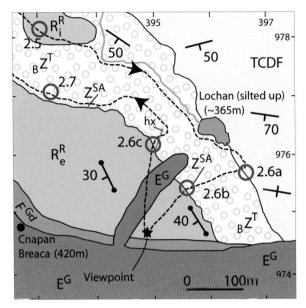

Figure 19. Geological sketch map of the Coire Dubh Breccias at the eastern end of the Northern Marginal Zone. Relationships with rhyodacite are seen at localities 2.6 and 2.7 (see pp. 148-49 for full key).

against the Marginal Gabbro of the ELI, the line of contact being marked by scattered exposures of intrusion breccia that are thought to have formed by back-veining of rhyodacite into the intruding gabbro (Dunham, 1964). The resistant rhyodacite forms a ridge that extends to Cnapan Breaca [NM 393 975], but the Marginal Gabbro has largely decayed to gravel. This ridge and the Cnapan Breaca summit area offer magnificent views of Hallival and the Eastern Layered Intrusion (Figures 19, 20).

About 150 m south-west of the lochan, there is a well-exposed contact between a small gabbro plug and rhyodacite. About 50 m north-west of the plug a 30 to 40 cm-thick tuffisite sheet cuts the breccia, but not the rhyodacite, and at several places west of the lochan a thin, impersistent layer of epiclastic sandstone separates rhyodacite from the main tuff-breccia succession to the north-east (Locality 2.6c). The numerous basic dykes at this locality post-date the rhyodacite, breccia and tuffisite.

Continue to a point about 150 m west-north-west of the silted-up lochan (Locality 2.6c), where there is a north-facing cliff that extends for nearly

43

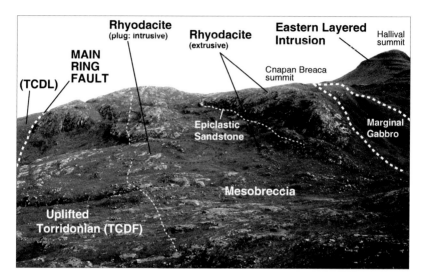

Figure 20. View of Coire Dubh from Meall Breac, with elements of the Northern Marginal Zone and the Eastern Layered Intrusion marked (see also Figure 4a).

0.5 km to the west-north-west. The cliff is formed by porphyritic rhyodacite, which overlies bedded tuffs, epiclastic sandstone and Coire Dubh Breccia.

Locality 2.7 [NM 3933 9769]

Coire Dubh – Epiclastic sandstone underlying tuffs at base of rhyodacite ash flows

The contact between the rhyodacite and the epiclastic sandstone crops out at several places along the base of the cliff (Figure 20). The sandstone may be up to 4 m in thickness. It is a coarse-grained gritty siliceous rock with very weak bedding and may exhibit some brecciation towards its base. The sandstone is overlain by bedded tuffs with suggestions of surge deposits; thin tuffaceous layers also occur within the lower part of the rhyodacite (Figure 21).

Locality 2.8 *c.* [NM 3915 9775]

Coire Dubh – rhyodacite fiamme deformed by 'bombs'

At the western end of Cnapan Breaca, rhyodacite, basal tuff beds, and bombs sagging into 'plastic' rhyodacite can be inspected, indicating beyond doubt that the rhyodacites of the Chapan Breaca sheet is extrusive in nature.

Descend into Coire Dubh, passing a small ruined dam [NM 3892 9782], and continue uphill for about 500 m in a west to west-north-west direction to the southern end of Meall Breac (at *c.* [NM 385 979]). The 100 to 150 m-wide zone of grass-covered gravel at the col exposes somewhat rotted Marginal Gabbro, bordered by the porphyritic rhyodacite of Meall Breac to the north and by layered ultrabasic rocks to the south (Figure 20).

Locality 2.9 [NM 3845 9797]

South end, Meall Breac – intrusion breccia at rhyodacite/gabbro contact

At the south end of Meall Breac, at 350 m altitude, the Marginal Gabbro is separated from porphyritic rhyodacite by a zone of intrusion breccia and some hybrid rocks (Dunham, 1964). In a short north to south traverse, rhyodacite with a dull matt surface passes into a zone of intrusion breccia in

Figure 21. Bedded tuffs at the base of the extrusive porphyritic rhyodacite, north side of Cnapan Breaca, Coire Dubh, near Locality 2.7. Scale: coin 2 cm diameter.

Figure 22. Attenuated fiamme in porphyritic rhyodacite ash flow, south-west end of Meall Breac (Locality 2.10).

which angular and subangular blocks of gabbro and rare feldspathic peridotite are enclosed by a network of pale-coloured felsic veins. Nearby, at [NM 3845 9798], a 1.5 m-wide, north-north-east-trending basalt dyke with conspicuous plagioclase phenocrysts (c. 1 cm diameter) is involved in the brecciation and veining. On approaching the contact zone from the north, the dyke changes colour from black to dull grey, there is a progressive increase in felsic veining, and eventually the dyke is seen to have disintegrated into large strips and blocks enclosed by rhyodacite. The dyke clearly intruded the porphyritic rhyodacite but it pre-dates the gabbros and ultrabasic rocks. Its progressive fragmentation in the intrusion breccia furnishes further evidence of local development of rheomorphic magma where felsic rocks have been intruded by hot, mafic magmas (see Summary of Geology). There are good views of the layered ultrabasic rocks on Hallival and on the northern slopes of Barkeval from this locality.

Locality 2.10 [NM 3837 9810]

South-west Meall Breac – deformed fiamme in rhyodacite ash flow

Continue downhill in a west-north-west direction until, after about 150 m, flat ground is reached at 310 m altitude. Coire Dubh Breccia and pale grey epiclastic sandstone crop out, overlain by porphyritic rhyodacite. Near the

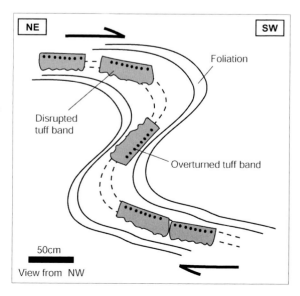

Figure 23. Field sketch of a broken and over-folded tuff band in a rhyodacite ignimbrite sheet, south-west Meall Breac. Note grading in tuff band indicates overturning during rheomorphic flow. Near Locality 2.10.

46

base of the rhyodacite, conspicuous fiamme dip to the east at a low angle (Figure 22). At the north end of the outcrop, a thin tuffaceous layer within the rhyodacite is overfolded, indicating that some downslope rheomorphic flow has occurred (Figure 23).

Locality 2.11 [NM 3825 9874]

Loch Gainmich – Am Màm Breccia underlying gabbro megablock

From Locality 2.10 walk north across wet, peaty ground to the eastern side of Loch Gainmhich (Figure 13) where a low cliff exposes a distinctive

Figure 24.
a. Portion of the Am Màm Breccias with blocks of coarse gabbro. Close to the north-east shore of Loch Gainmhich. NB: hammer at bottom centre.
b. Block of gabbro intruded by dacitic matrix of the Am Màm Breccias, in

between Meall Breac and Am Màm hills. Scale: hammer shaft c. 30 cm.
c. Representative view of Am Màm breccia matrix containing a variety of lobate enclaves and sedimentary and metamorphic xenoliths. Scale: coin is 2 cm in diameter.

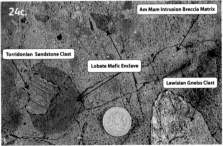

47

breccia containing large gabbro clasts (Figure 24). The breccia has a pale cream-coloured, crystalline felsic matrix with scattered plagioclase and pyroxene crystals and small (1–2 cm diameter) rounded areas of a mafic rock. This breccia, termed the Am Màm Breccia, differs significantly from the Coire Dubh Breccia in that it has a distinctly igneous matrix and has a very varied clast population that includes abundant igneous material and gneiss. The breccia has a sharp contact against overlying gabbro, which crops out over an area 100 m across.

Locality 2.12 [NM 3825 9873]
East of Loch Gainmich – gabbro/gneiss contact, megablock in Am Màm Breccia

100 m east of Loch Gainmhich the gabbro has a fine-grained contact against a strip of thermally metamorphosed gneiss. This is probably a primary intrusive contact. The more abundant amphibolitic parts of the gneiss are altered to pyroxene hornfels, whereas the felsic parts show signs of partial melting. Hereabouts apophyses of dark-coloured porphyritic rhyodacite intrude the gneiss, gabbro and Am Màm Breccias.

Locality 2.13 [NM 3830 9885]
Am Màm – Am Màm Breccia with gabbro, gneiss and sandstone clasts

The breccia should be examined on the north-east side of Am Màm (the 'Three Loch Hill' of Dunham, 1968) where large blocks of gneiss, gritty sandstone and gabbro (some of which are extremely coarse grained) are prominent constituents (Figures 24a, b), together with smaller, finer grained mafic enclaves (Figure 24c). A north-north-east-trending porphyritic basalt dyke intrudes the breccia and is offset dextrally by an east–west fault (splay of the MRF system?).

From this point a detour can be made to visit the Priomh-lochs area. This adds about 3 km to the day's walking. (See below, Localities 2.16–2.19.)

Locality 2.14 [NM3856 9867]

East of Am Mam – gabbro of megablock cut by Am Màm Breccia
and rhyodacite

Descend to the valley east of Am Màm where gabbro forms a knoll north of
several shallow lochans (the 'Three Lochs' of Dunham, 1968). Porphyritic
rhyodacite cuts the gabbro on its southern side, as do cream-coloured felsic
veins and thin dykes similar in appearance to the matrix of the Am Màm
Breccia, which again crops out on the north side of the knoll. This large area
of gabbro (100 x 50 m) lacks any indications of fine-grained, chilled margins
and appears to be a megablock within the breccias rather than a plug (cf.
Dunham, 1968).

Locality 2.15 [NM 3870 9860]

North Meall Breac – Am Màm Breccia cut by, and grades into, rhyodacite

Continuing east, follow a rough path that contours around the hillside to a
shelf at 100 m altitude at the north end of Meall Breac. The steep western end
of the shelf exposes a thin north–south dolerite dyke packed with dull, black,
rounded fragments of pyroxenite, spinel-bearing feldspathic peridotite,
peridotite and large magnesian olivines. The dark colour is caused by patchy
brown clouding of the abundant olivine (cf. the picrite dyke at Locality 4.9).
Am Màm Breccia crops out over much of the shelf and is cut by a broad,
wedge-like dyke of porphyritic rhyodacite that tapers to the east. A short,
shallow valley on the southern limit of the shelf is bordered on its south side
by a gabbro plug and by a sloping outcrop of intrusive breccia to the north. The
breccia contains fragments of fine-grained sandstone together with rounded
to subangular gabbro clasts and rare pieces of feldspathic peridotite.
Breccias towards the eastern end of the shelf are bordered by, and appear to
grade into, porphyritic rhyodacite. To the north, the steep northern face of
the shelf exposes much gneiss in an elongate (east–west) area. This possibly
represents a sliver caught between parts of the Main Ring Fault or, alternatively, another large block entrained in the Am Màm Breccia.

To return to Kinloch, continue downhill in a south-east direction for
about 450 m until the deer fence gate near the hydro-electric dam is reached
(Locality 2.2), then follow the path down the glen. (Total distance is c. 7 km
distance, of which 3 km are the walk back from Am Màm.)

OPTIONAL: Traverse west, towards Priomh-lochs

From the north-west side of Am Màm (Locality 2.13) traverse along the edge of Loch Gainmhich to gabbro crags at the north end of the loch.

Locality 2.16 [NM 3805 9895]

Loch Gainmich – small intrusive plug of gabbro inside Main Ring Fault

A small plug of gabbro is situated just inside the Main Ring Fault. The gabbro is relatively unaltered and much finer grained than the gabbro involved with the Am Màm Breccia. Skirt the southern end of Loch Bealach Mhic Nèill (Figure 13) and follow the western shore for 200 m to a small gabbro mass surrounded by gritty sandstone, then walk north-west for 150 m to a prominent north–south ridge of feldspathic peridotite with excellent examples of steeply dipping matrix banding (Dunham, 1965).

Locality 2.17 [NM 3735 9900]

Ridge east of Priomh-lochs – 'matrix banding' in peridotite tongue

The ridge is formed by a tongue of peridotite that extends north from the Layered Centre to cut the Main Ring Fault (Figure 13). Follow the ridge to the south for about 250 m, observing variation in the matrix-banding structures (Dunham, 1965), then walk west over sandstone outcrops for about 250 m to a point 170 m east-north-east of the peaty ground between the Priomh-lochs (Figure 13).

Locality 2.18 [NM 3715 9876]

Priomh-lochs – faulted and unconformable relationships of gritty sandstone to gneiss

The coarse sandstone hereabouts belongs to the Fiachanis Gritty Sandstone Member (TCDF) and is in contact with gneisses, which form extensive exposures either side of the Priomh-lochs. The boundary is probably an

unconformity, complicated by minor faulting. The gneisses nearest the peridotite tongue have been thermally metamorphosed with indications of some melting in the leucocratic variants. However, the deformation and contortion of gneissose banding seen in many exposures pre-dates the Paleocene (Holness and Isherwood, 2003; cf. Emeleus 1997; Figure 25).

Figure 25.
Banded Lewisian granodioritic biotite gneisses with amphibolitic layers, near Priomh-lochs. (Photo: Emeleus / BGS © NERC)

Locality 2.19 [NM 367 994]

North of Priomh-lochs – explosion breccia injected along line of Main Ring Fault

Pass to the north of the Priomh-lochs and continue in a north-west direction for about 700 m until a prominent west-north-west-trending ridge is reached. The traverse crosses extensive gneiss outcrops, together with gabbro and ill-exposed microgranite; the gabbros are of late date since they cut the Main Ring Fault. The ridge marks the position of a strip of explosion breccias parallel to, and just inside, the Main Ring Fault. The breccia differs from the Am Màm Breccia since it contains fragments of porphyritic rhyodacite in addition to gabbro. It is cut by small rhyodacite intrusions. From here, either return to the north side of Loch Gainmhich and resume the itinerary (see above), or continue a short distance downhill in a north-westerly direction to the track that leads back to Kinloch (which is about 4 km distant).

Excursion 3
Hallival and Askival

HIGHLIGHTS

Components of the Eastern Layered Intrusion will be examined during this excursion, which will focus on Units 8–15 in the upper part of the layered succession of troctolites ('allivalites'), gabbroic rocks and feldspathic peridotites described in the classic paper by G. M. Brown (1956). Excellent examples of small-scale layered structures occur in the troctolites and adjoining chromite seams and an enigmatic 'wavy horizon' (pyroxene cumulate overlying troctolite) is seen.

The full excursion is about 11 km in length and involves climbing to the summit of Hallival (722 m). It should not be undertaken in bad weather, but reserved for a fine day when the views from the summit of Hallival are spectacular. The excursion may be extended to include Askival (812 m), the highest peak on Rum, adding another 200 m of climbing and about 2 km distance.

Taking the same route up to Coire Dubh as for Excursion 2, pass through the deer fence gate and follow the path on the west side of the burn for about 500 m (Figure 26).

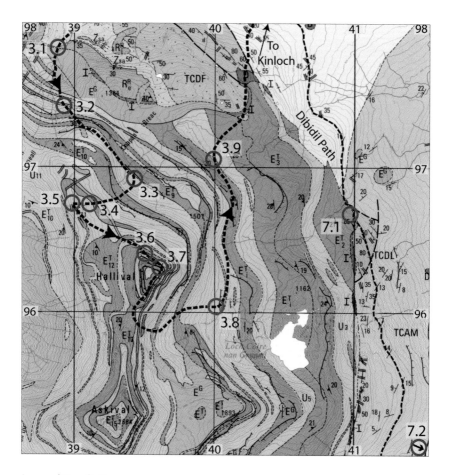

Locality 3.1 [NM 3892 9782]

Coire Dubh dam – intrusion breccia on edge
of Eastern Layered Intrusion

Scattered exposures of intrusion breccia and baked Coire Dubh
Breccia near the remains of a small dam indicate the proximity
of the Marginal Gabbro. The grass-covered slopes to the west
and south-east define the outcrop of the easily weathered
gabbro, which dips north at a moderate angle (Figure 20).
Follow the path across a flat, marshy area and continue uphill
for about 200 m in a south-south-east direction.

Figure 26.
Geological map
of Excursion 3:
Eastern Layered
Intrusion, Hallival
and Askival (see
pp. 148-49 for full
key; based on SNH
1:20,000 solid
geology map;
©SNH).

53

Figure 27. Chromite seams (along the contact between light anorthositic troctolite and peridotite) in an exposure (plan view) at the base of Unit 8, Eastern Layered Intrusion, Locality 3.2. Scale: hammer shaft *c.* 30 cm.

Figure 28. Undulatory 'wavy contact' between dark pyroxene-rich (gabbroic) and pale plagioclase-rich (troctolite) layers in Unit 9. Locality 3.3, shelf north of Hallival. Scale: hammer shaft *c.* 30 cm.

Locality 3.2 [NM 3896 9742]

Coire Dubh – chromite seams and anorthositic troctolite at Unit 7/8 boundary

Troctolite at the top of Unit 7 forms a prominent line of crags at about 370 m altitude. A thin skin of peridotite (the base of Unit 8) covers much of the back of the adjacent shelf. The junction between the units is complex: a thin layer containing anorthosite, chromite seams and peridotite overlies troctolite with small-scale layering and signs of slumping (Figure 27; Bedard *et al.*, 1988) and small 'outliers' of peridotite, a few centimetres in diameter, are scattered across the shelf. The 'outliers' are separated from the anorthosite and troctolite by a thin chromite-rich layer that is generally a few millimetres thick, but which thickens locally to 1–2 cm in downward-projecting 'sags' or 'potholes' (cf. Lee, 1981).

Continue gently uphill in a south-east direction, skirting round a prominent bluff [NM 3922 9728] at about 440 m elevation. On rounding the bluff a wide shelf in the Unit 9 troctolite extends for 400 m to the south-east, at 430–440 m altitude. There is small-scale layering in the troctolite which is also generally quite well laminated. The troctolite is overlain by a laminated gabbroic cumulate and there is a dense, laminated concentration of dark green clinopyroxene along the undulating contact (Figure 28). Locally the wavy contact extends across the main mineral lamination.

Locality 3.3 [NM 3950 9694]

North of Hallival – 'wavy contact' within Unit 9,
at troctolite/gabbro boundary

Weathering of the rock into several low scarps has provided beautiful exposures of this remarkable 'wavy contact' between troctolite and overlying gabbroic cumulates (Figure 28). These must not be hammered. The relationships between the troctolite and gabbroic cumulates and the significance of the 'wavy' contact have been interpreted in various ways. Young and Donaldson (1985) suggested spontaneous formation at the interface between two fluids with reversed density gradients; Volker and Upton (1990) interpreted similar structures in Unit 14 on Trollaval to be flame structures caused by loading; whereas Bedard *et al.* (1988) were of the opinion that the overlying pyroxene-rich bytownite gabbro formed metasomatically from bytownite troctolite (allivalite) permeated by basaltic melt (see also Bedard and Sparks, 1991 and Upton and Volker, 1991). A complicating factor is a thick peridotite sill which underlies much of the shelf but transgresses through the troctolite at its southern end (*c.* [NM 3975 9685]), and has recently been invoked as a cause of metasomatic mobilisation of pyroxene, resulting in a frozen undulatory mobilisation front (see Holness *et al.*, 2005; Holness, 2005, 2007; Holness *et al.*, 2007a, b).

The slopes to the south-west of Locality 3.3, backing the Unit 9 shelf, are formed of Unit 10 peridotite which is also well exposed in a near continuous section in the prominent bluff at the north end of the shelf [NM 392 971] (e.g. Brown, 1956; Tait, 1985; Palacz and Tait, 1985; Bedard *et al.*, 1988). Ascend these slopes to reach the prominent shelf at about 530 m altitude on the northern flank of Hallival.

Locality 3.4 [NM 391 968]

Shelf north-west of Hallival – gabbroic sheet intruding Unit 12 troctolite

The shelf has good, if scattered, exposures of a well-developed, west-south-west-dipping, 1–3 mm-thick, chromite-rich seam between Unit 11 troctolite and Unit 12 peridotite. The ultrabasic rocks in this area are intruded by a steeply inclined gabbroic sheet, but it will be noted that minor intrusions are uncommon when compared with exposures examined on Excursion 2.

Locality 3.5 [NM 3895 9679]

Shelf north-west of Hallival – classic Unit 11/12 boundary
with chromite seam

The Unit 11/12 chromite seam described and figured by Brown (1956) is
about 100 m farther west, where it crops out at about 510 m altitude,
overlooking Atlantic Corrie. Exposure is good, and in a few exposures
peridotite appears to replace troctolite; note the discontinuous nature of the
seam. (On no account should *in-situ* material be removed from this classic
locality, nor should the outcrops be defaced by hammering.)

Locality 3.6 *c.* [NM 394 965]

North of Hallival summit – deformation and slumping in layered troctolites

Proceed south-east for *c.* 400 m to the base of the cliffs on the north side of
Hallival. The small-scale layering in the thick troctolite of Unit 13 is
commonly disturbed by slumping (Figure 29). Thin disconnected layers
of anorthositic troctolite have been tightly folded, and the rocks in

Figure 29. Slump structure
in Unit 13 troctolite, Eastern
Layered Intrusion, locality
3.6, Halival. Scale: hammer
shaft *c.* 30 cm.

56

general show signs of disruption and shearing. Thin layers and stringers of peridotite appear intrusive or, in some instances, to have partially replaced troctolite.

Close to Locality 3.6 a fairly well-defined path leads to the summit of Hallival, passing up through Units 13 and 14, where further examples of disturbed troctolites and apparently intrusive peridotites occur.

Locality 3.7 [NM 3953 9626]

Hallival summit – panoramic views of Eigg, north-west Highlands, Skye and Outer Isles

Around the Hallival summit area (Figures 30, 31), there are further examples of intrusive (and/or slumped?) peridotites in the troctolite (Renner and Palacz, 1987) and a thin, pale-grey dyke of intermediate composition cuts the layered rocks a short distance to the south. Hallival provides an excellent viewpoint on a clear day. Nearby, to the south, are the layered rocks of Askival; to the north, the west-dipping Torridonian strata on Mullach Mòr, with the Skye Cuillin and Red Hills in the background and the Applecross hills in the far distance. The Isle of Eigg with the spectacular pitchstone ridge of the Sgurr lies to the east (Hudson and Allwright, 2003), with the high mountains beyond Loch Nevis and Loch Morar in the

Figure 30.
Rhythmically modally layered troctolite with small-scale, intra-layer slump structures. Note the small-scale slump structures in the upper part of the section, and the irregular upper surfaces of thin, in-weathering brown peridotite layers near the top and base, indicating corrosion by underlying peridotite. Section is about 2 m in height. South-east side of Hallival.

Figure 31. View of west-dipping layered units in the upper part of the Eastern Layered Intrusion, south side of Hallival. Scale: about 120 m from grassy col to Hallival summit. Photo taken from Askival.

Figure 32. Rockfall on east side of Hallival. The large block at the base of the rockfall (circled) is about 5 m in height. Locality 3.8.

background, amongst which the distinctive outline of Ben Nevis may be visible (over 80 km distant). To the west, the rough ground formed by peridotites and gabbros in Glen Harris, and on Barkeval and An Dornabac contrasts strongly with the smooth scree-, grass- and boulder-covered slopes of Ard Nev and other microgranite hills, while step-weathering lava flows are visible on Orval and Fionchra. Far to the west of Rum, beyond Harris Bay, the lighthouse on Oigh-sgeir may be visible. This is built on pitchstone similar to that which forms the Sgurr of Eigg. The lavas of Canna and south-west Skye lie to the north-west and, beyond them, the line of the Outer Isles may be visible. The views are a considerable reward for climbing Hallival, which should be visited on a fine day, even at the expense of disturbing an otherwise apparently logical sequence of excursions.

From Hallival the return to Kinloch may be made by retracing the path down to the shoulder on the north-west side of the hill and continuing in a north-west to west-north-west direction until Bealach Bairc-mheall is reached. From the col [NM 3865 9707], at 466 m altitude, a rather indistinct path leads down to the flat area at the base of Coire Dubh (near Locality 3.1) and back to Kinloch by the same route as was taken earlier in the day. Alternatively, and preferably in dry, fine weather, take the well-defined but steep and rocky path south-south-west off Hallival down to the col [NM 3946 9592] at 600 m altitude, then descend eastwards into Coire nan Grunnd. However, if the Askival summit area is to be visited, the easiest route from the col is to contour in a southerly direction along the base of the cliffs on the eastern side of Askival for about 700 m from which point an ill-defined path climbs in a generally west-north-west direction through the troctolite crags to the summit. There are excellent examples of slumping in Unit 14 troctolite on this path (Figures 29, 30; Brown, 1956). Major folding in troctolite, attributed to slumping, is also seen in cliffs north of the summit (Emeleus, 1997). The views from Askival equal those obtained from Hallival.

Locality 3.8 c.[NM 400 961]

Coire nan Grunnd – details of troctolite layering displayed in fallen blocks

The three-dimensional details of troctolite layering are beautifully displayed in house-sized blocks scattered across the floor of Coire nan Grunnd (Figure 32). There are also excellent views of the layered rocks on the south-east face of Hallival (Figure 31), where structures suggesting disruption of peridotite in (slumped?) troctolite are visible. Binoculars are a distinct advantage here; the remains of recent spectacular rock falls on this side of the mountain bring one to realise just how unstable these slopes can be (Figure 32). From Coire nan Grunnd continue north-north-east at about 350 m altitude, passing grey-weathering gabbro sheets intruded more or less conformably into the layered ultrabasic rocks. After about 1 km, pass over a low col [NM 402 968] and continue north into the broad, shallow valley in the headwaters of the Allt Mòr na h-Uamha (around [NM 402 970]).

Locality 3.9 [NM 397 972]

Allt Mòr na h-Uamha – rafts of hornfelsed basalt in layered troctolite

Inclusions of ultrabasic rocks and of fine-grained highly hornfelsed mafic rocks occur within gabbro exposed in slabs to the north of the stream. The altered basalt may represent rafts of basaltic lava (from the Eigg Lava Formation) which have subsided from the intrusion roof onto the contemporary floor. Pale-coloured spots rich in plagioclase and containing hydro-garnet are interpreted to be metamorphosed amygdales (Faithfull, 1985). Continue for about 400 m in a direction slightly east of north, passing east of the Cnapan Breaca ridge at about 350 m altitude, where easily weathered Marginal Gabbro bordering the ultrabasic rocks is exposed in contact with baked sedimentary rocks [NM 402 976]. At this point, a somewhat ill-defined path leads in a northerly direction to a gate in the deer fence. From the fence, continue north-east for about 350 m across rough, peaty ground to join the Dibidil–Kinloch path. Alternatively, from Locality 3.8, follow the north bank of the Allt Mòr na h-Uamha down over moderately steep rock-, grass- and heather-covered slopes to the Kinloch–Dibidil path where there is another deer fence gate [NM 4047 9743]. Walk north along the path to Kinloch (c. 2.5 km from the gate).

Excursion 4

The Central Intrusion

HIGHLIGHTS

(Excursion 4A) Exposures in the Central Intrusion close to the road to Harris and to the west and south of the Long Loch include excellent examples of layered troctolite, apparent erosion of troctolite by 'debris flows' crowded with peridotite 'cobbles' and 'pebbles', and blocks of layered troctolite and feldspathic peridotite ranging in size from a metre to many tens of metres in breccias with highly disturbed feldspathic peridotite matrices. Further south, unusual feldspar and olivine growth structures occur in the Central Intrusion and also in the Western Layered Intrusion, which may be visited in the latter part of the day. The excursion may be extended (Excursion 4B) by continuing to Harris Bay (a long walk), where layering in gabbros extends to within a few metres of the contact with microgranite and where the complicated contact between the Western Layered Intrusion and the Western Granite is excellently exposed in sea cliffs.

Follow the Kilmory road from Kinloch for 3 km then take the south fork towards Harris (Figure 33).

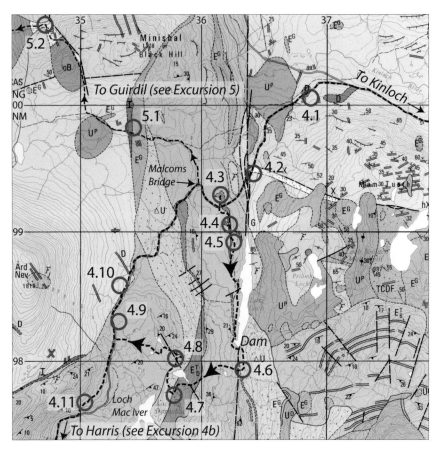

Figure 33. Geological map of Excursion 4A, Central Rum, covering the northern end of the Central Intrusion and adjoining layered areas of the Eastern Layered Intrusion and Western Layered Intrusion (see pp. 148-49 for full key; based on SNH 1:20,000 solid geology map; © SNH).

Excursion 4A

Locality 4.1 [NG 3696 0016]

Harris road near Kilmory fork – quarry shows sandstone
baked by dolerite plug

A small roadstone quarry on the south side of the road exposes a dolerite plug with adjoining bleached, fractured and baked sandstone. The alteration is typical of that encountered next to the dolerite and gabbro plugs found throughout northern Rum. From this locality the distinctive, localised grey scree derived from fragmented sandstone next to a substantial gabbro plug may be seen on the western slopes of Mullach Mòr, about 2 km to the north-north-east (at [NG 376 012]). Another 400 m along the road a contact between peridotite and baked sandstone is exposed in a stream bed above a bridge [NG 3672 0000], but the degree of alteration appears much less than that found adjacent to gabbro or dolerite plugs.

Figure 34. Peridotite blocks ('dropstones') with deformed layering (impact structures?) in layered troctolite of the Central Intrusion. Scale: pen 13 cm. Locality 4.3.

Locality 4.2 [NM 3639 9944]

Bridge south of Long Loch – evidence for Long Loch Fault
in riverside exposures

The Long Loch Fault follows the course of the Kilmory River at the bridge, and fractured, sheared and crushed peridotite, microgranite, sandstone and gneiss are exposed in the river bed hereabouts. The latest movement on the fault post-dates the central complex, but the fault is thought to have had significant pre-central complex movement. Thermally altered gneiss (pyroxene hornfels) crops out in sparse exposures in a low, east-facing scarp about 100 m west of the bridge. Continue along the road to a shallow east–west valley through peridotite [NM 3617 9919].

Locality 4.3 [NM 3615 9929]

North of Harris road – layering in troctolite deformed by 'dropstones'

Blocks of troctolite are enclosed in feldspathic peridotite about 150 m to the north of the road. Distortion of the layering around the blocks resembles that seen where dropstones have impacted into bedded sedimentary rocks (Figure 34).

South of the road a low, 'whaleback' ridge extends north–south for about 500 m on the west side of the Long Loch. Westward-dipping (30–40°) layered troctolites are magnificently exposed on flat, glaciated surfaces along much of the length of the ridge. They are interpreted to be within a 'megablock' that spalled off the adjoining Eastern Layered Intrusion, subsiding into magma rising along feeders located on the early Long Loch Fault.

Locality 4.4 [NM 3620 9908]

'Whaleback' west of Long Loch – depositional and erosional sedimentary structures in troctolite

Troctolite seen on the glaciated slabs contain slump, scour, 'flame', and graded-bedding structures resembling those found in clastic sedimentary

64

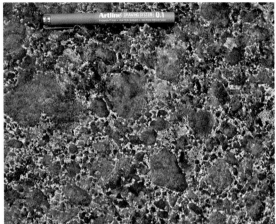

Figure 35. Layered troctolite in the Central Intrusion. Locality 4.4, 'whale-back' ridge west of Long Loch.

Figure 36. Detail of the peridotite 'cobble' avalanche deposit as in Figure 35. Locality 4.4. Central Intrusion. Scale: pen c.15 cm.

rocks (Figure 35). The upper surface of the layered structures appears to have been eroded by a 'debris avalanche' of peridotite laden with rounded pebble- and cobble-sized peridotite fragments which also show some size-grading (Figure 36).

Locality 4.5 [NM 3623 9893]

'Whaleback' – layering in troctolite, transgressed by underlying peridotite

Particularly good three-dimensional examples of the layering occur in a low cliff on the east side of the ridge (Figure 37). At this locality, the troctolite is underlain by brown peridotite which has finger-like protrusions extending upwards into the layered rocks (cf. Locality 6.2). Towards the south end of the ridge, the peridotite that underlies layered troctolite at Locality 4.5 cross-cuts and locally replaces troctolite.

Continue to the south end of the Long Loch [NM 3627 9810] (but note that the stream at [NG 3628 9853] may be difficult to cross after heavy rain), cross the dam and continue a further 200 m to the south-south-east.

65

Figure 37. Graded and slumped layered troctolite cut by thin basalt sheets at the east side of the 'whaleback' ridge. Note how the brown peridotite at the base of the section cuts across the layering and sends irregular finger-like projections into the overlying troctolite (see arrows). Locality 4.5 Central Intrusion, 'whaleback' west of Long Loch. Rock-face is c. 2–5m high.

Figure 38. Large triangular block of layered troctolite and peridotite enclosed in disturbed troctolite draped over the top. Locality 4.6, about 120m south-south-east of Long Loch. Central Intrusion. Scale: hammer shaft at left centre 30cm.

Locality 4.6 [NM 3635 9792]

South of Long Loch – layered troctolite/peridotite blocks in deformed layered peridotite

The layered peridotites exposed in small cliffs and scarps are extremely deformed around large blocks of troctolite and layered peridotite that have collapsed into them. In some instances the blocks, which range from metres to tens of metres in size, are themselves layered, and individual blocks may preserve a record of magmatic sedimentation, slumping, corrosion and replacement (Figure 38). The blocks are thought to have avalanched off the edge of the Eastern Layered Intrusion during emplacement of the Central Intrusion, deforming the poorly consolidated feldspathic peridotite cumulates. About 150 m to the south, across a small stream, steeply dipping layered troctolite exposed in an elongate (north–south) knoll is another example of one of these megablocks.

Cross the 50 m-wide, steep-sided valley marking the course of the Long

Figure 39. Pronounced, narrow trench eroded along the course of the Long Loch Fault. (Near Locality 4.6.) Looking south. Central Intrusion, south of the Long Loch.

Loch Fault (Figure 39) and walk uphill for 300m in a westerly direction, until the outlet of a lochan is reached at [NM 3588 9782]. This traverse crosses part of the Central Intrusion characterised by approximately north–south zones of peridotite breccias (Donaldson, 1975), commonly crowded with blocks of peridotite and troctolite, some of which are layered (Figure 40). This traverse crosses part of the complex feeder zone to the Layered Centre of the Rum Central Complex (Figure 43).

Locality 4.7 [NM 3569 9769]

Loch an Dornabac – poikilo-macro-spherulitic structures in peridotite of Central Intrusion

These structures are on a shelf about 200m to the south-west of the lochan. Here, spectacular bunches of radiating, bifurcating rays of plagioclase crystals occur in feldspathic peridotite (Figure 41). The feldspars are up to 40cm in length and enclose innumerable small olivine crystals. These are the type examples of *poikilo-macro-spherulitic* structures (Donaldson *et al.*, 1973) and have grown *in situ*, possibly from a hydrous feldspathic peridotite magma. About 50m to the east-north-east, olivine lamination in peridotite is deformed around peridotite inclusions.

67

Figure 40.
a. Portion of ultrabasic intrusion breccia (conduit fill) in the Central Intrusion, Abhainn Rangail. Scale: hammer shaft 30 cm. Locality 4.18.

b. Breccia of layered troctolite blocks in a feldspathic peridotite matrix (debris avalanche type), Central Intrusion, Harris track near Locality 4.7.

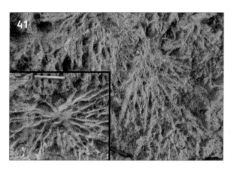

Figure 41.
Radiating rays of plagioclase in feldspathic peridotite ('poikilo-macro-spherulitic structures') in Central Intrusion east of Loch MacIver (Loch an Dornabac). [NM3569 9772], Locality 4.7. Scale: pen 13 cm.

INSET: Close up of a poikilo-macro-spherulite.

Locality 4.8 [NM 3576 9800]

North of Loch an Dornabac – small-scale layering in peridotite of Western Layered Intrusion

South-east-dipping, finely layered peridotite belonging to the Ard Mheall member (Figure 33) at the top of the Western Layered Intrusion forms the cliffs 300 m north-north-east of Locality 4.6. The contact with the Central Intrusion is exposed a short distance to the north on the north-north-west-trending ridge.

To regain the Harris road (at about [NM 3527 9810]), walk 500 m west-north-west across wet peaty ground with scattered peridotite exposures. At this point, either (A) return to Kinloch along the road (*c.* 5 km) or (B) continue south through the Western Layered Intrusion towards its outer contact with the Western Granite at Harris.

Locality 4.9 [NM 353 984]

Road east of Ard Nev – dense, black picrite dyke intruding peridotite

Following option 'A', walking towards Kinloch, there are several shallow abandoned quarries in crumbling peridotite on the east side of the track. Loose blocks of a dense, matt-black picrite come from a badly weathered picrite dyke. The highly magnesian picrite contains an abundance of forsteritic olivines (Fo_{93}); (McClurg, 1982; Upton et al., 2002).

Locality 4.10 [NM 3540 9870]

Roadside north-east of Ard Nev – baked microgranite
and (nearby) altered dolerite, near peridotite

Farther along the road, baked microgranite (the Western Granite) is exposed in contact with peridotite. Off the road some 70 m to the west a thick, north-west-trending dolerite dyke intrudes the microgranite. This dyke, which forms a low ridge, has also been altered by the nearby peridotite. Continue along the road to Kinloch.

If proceeding towards Harris (option 'B', Figures 44 and 45), follow the road south for about 200 m, then contour around the hillside for a further 200 m, passing derelict eagle cages on the way.

Locality 4.11 [NM 3502 9772]

East of Ard Mheall – harrisitic structures in peridotite,
some showing erosional features

Excellent harrisitic structures (Harker, 1908; Donaldson, 1974, 1976; O'Driscoll et al., 2007a) occur in layered peridotites of the Ard Mheall member (Western Layered Intrusion), exposed in a series of low, west-facing crags (Figure 42). Elongate olivine crystals in the peridotite appear to have grown upwards for 5–20 cm from a substrate of granular olivine. In places, dark, platy olivine crystals are arranged in an imbricate manner, suggesting they have been broken from the tips of harrisitic structures and redistributed by magmatic currents (Figures 42, 43). Walk downhill to the road and continue south for 2 km. Exposures are few and the ground is largely drift covered.

Figure 42. Rhythmic harrisite and 'sedimentary' layers in feldspathic peridotite. Sedimentary layers contain recycled harrisite crystals. Scale: hammer shaft c.15 cm. Locality 4.11, Western Layered Intrusion, east of Ard Mheall.

INSET: Fragments of dark harrisite olivines that have been 'reworked' by sedimentary processes (see arrows).

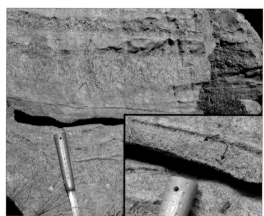

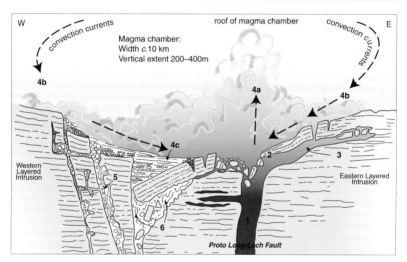

Figure 43. Schematic representation of possible events leading to the formation of the Central Intrusion. Periodic replenishments of picritic magma (1) rejuvenated the magma chamber causing sliding and slumping (2) and intruded laterally into earlier cumulates (3). Magma fountaining into the chamber (4a) flows off the roof and down the sides as crystal-laden, gravity-driven currents (4b), dislodging crystal mushes as they move, then spread across the floor, reworking cumulate debris and depositing this material and primary crystals on the floor (4c). Movement on faults was accompanied by magma injection, thermal erosion of earlier rocks and their fragmentation to form breccia zones (5). Slides of coherent blocks of cumulate across partly liquefied cumulate led to spectacular slump mélanges (6). (Emeleus et al. [1996]. After Emeleus and Bell [2005].) (© NERC)

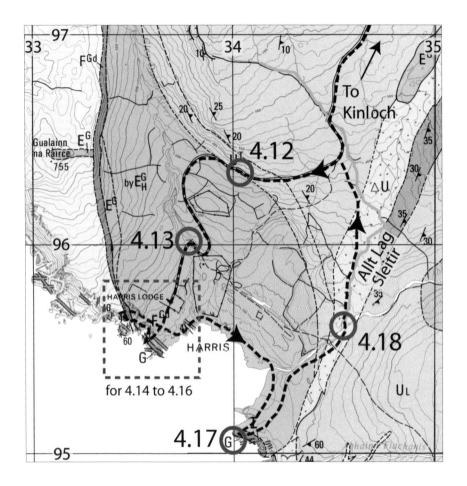

Excursion 4B

Locality 4.12 [NM 341 963] (Figure 44)

North of Harris Bay – roadside exposures of harrisitic structures

Roadside exposures in crags at the transition between the gabbroic Harris Bay member and the overlying peridotites of the Ard Mheall member contain excellent examples of harrisitic structures (Wadsworth, 1961).

Figure 44.
Geological map
of the Harris Bay
area, Excursion 4b.
(See pp. 148-49
for full key; based
on SNH 1:20,000
solid geology
map; © SNH.)

71

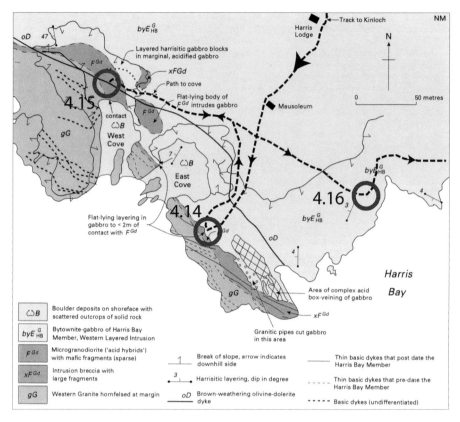

Figure 45. Geological map of western Harris Bay, showing details of the contact between the Western Layered Intrusion and the Western Granite (after Emeleus, 1997 / © NERC) (see pp. 148-49 for full key).

Locality 4.13 [NM 3377 9602]

Harris – spectacular layering in gabbros north of bridge

On the approach to Harris, strongly contrasting, flat-lying, feldspathic and mafic layering occurs in gabbro on the east side of the Glen Duian Burn, close to the bridge. Continue to Harris Lodge [NM 3366 9574], and cross the flat ground south to the low cliffs about 100 m south-south-west of the mausoleum.

Locality 4.14 [NM 3350 9560]

West end, Harris Bay – contact of layered gabbro
(with harrisite) and microgranite

To the south-south-west of the mausoleum, the layered rocks are separated from microgranite by a thin zone of gabbro, and basic and acid hybrid rocks. There is a limited development of intrusion breccia and some intricate felsic net-veining of the gabbro (Greenwood, 1987). Flat-lying harrisitic layers (Figure 46) crop out to within a metre or so of the contact zone; some layers appear to bifurcate. Numerous hornfelsed basaltic dykes cut the microgranite, and dykes and sheets are common in the microgranite exposed in the sea cliffs to the north-west (Figure 47). It is difficult to verify that the dykes are truncated by the mafic rocks, since most appear to die out close to the contact, but the dykes are commonly cut by thin felsic veins in the contact zone. Microgranite at and near the contact has a dull, matt-grey appearance, contrasting with the usual cream-white colour elsewhere in the

Figure 46. Layer of coarse-grained harrisitic olivine in bytownite gabbro of the Western Layered Intrusion, Harris Bay. Scale: hammer shaft c. 35 cm.

Figure 47. Sea-cliffs of granite intruded by numerous north-west-trending basaltic dykes and inclined sheets. Western Granite on the west side of Harris Bay. The shelf at the top of the cliffs is a pre-Late Devensian rock platform.

73

Western Granite. Thin section examination shows that the rock has been extensively recrystallised; fingerprint textures are present in the plagioclase phenocrysts and aggregates of hypersthene, augite and opaque minerals pseudomorph the original mafic minerals.

Locality 4.15 [NM 3348 9565]

Cove west of Harris Bay – contact between gabbro and hybridised microgranite

West of the mausoleum a path leads down to a cove where the contact zone is exposed (Figures 48a, b). Cliffs on the west of the cove expose grey microgranite cut by numerous sheets and dykes of dolerite and basalt striking approximately parallel to the coast (i.e. north-west). The microgranite is in contact with a felsic hybrid rock characterised by an acicular development of mafic minerals. Near the west end of a small cliff next to the path on the north side of the cove, the felsic hybrid is in fairly well-defined contact with contaminated (silicified) gabbro characterised by a patchy pegmatitic crystallisation. A few metres east of the contact the silicified gabbro contains xenoliths of layered gabbroic rock. Faint layering occurs in gabbroic rocks at the eastern end of this face and a thick band of gabbro, similar to that in the xenoliths in the contaminated gabbro, crops out at path level.

The contact between layered gabbros of the Harris Bay Member and microgranite belonging to the Western Granite is also extremely well exposed at the east end of Harris Bay. To reach this locality from the mausoleum, cross the Glen Duian burn near the shore (or go upstream and use the road bridge [Locality 4.13] if the river is high), and continue east, either along the layered gabbro benches on the rocky foreshore or walk along the low cliffs, on the magnificent late-glacial storm beaches at the back of the bay. There is a bridge over the Abhainn Rangail at [NM 3450 9555], although it is normally possible to cross the river close to the shore. The contact is exposed on a promontory about 350 m to the south and is most easily approached over the grass-covered storm beach. Note that here, and elsewhere, the boulders and cobbles in these beach deposits consist largely of microgranite and (Torridonian) sandstone. Gabbro and peridotite are virtually absent, presumably having disintegrated under the turbulent conditions when the beaches formed.

74

Figure 48.
a. Tongues of harrisitic gabbro in bytownite gabbro (Western Layered Intrusion) extending into hybrid granite zone to the left. Locality 4.15, Cove west of mausoleum, Harris Bay.

b. Close up of contact, about 8 m to left of person in Figure 48a. Scale: hammer c. 30 cm. The contact is highly irregular in detail, with some intrusion breccia in places.

Locality 4.16 [NM 373 958]

Harris Bay – shelves eroded in well-layered gabbro

Slabs and cliffs on this part of the coast and for some hundreds of metres to the east, provide the best exposures of the gabbroic rocks of the Harris Bay member, including good examples of harrisitic structures (cf. Donaldson *et al.*, 1973; Figures 7, 46).

Locality 4.17 [NM 3405 9505]

East end Harris Bay – intrusion breccia at gabbro/microgranite contact

Gabbro with flat-lying layering occupies most of the promontory, but a small area of baked, bleached microgranite crops out on the south side. The gabbro and microgranite are separated by a zone of intrusion breccia

75

several metres in width, consisting of angular and subangular blocks of basalt, dolerite, gabbro and rare peridotite, from 0.5 to 2 m in diameter, in a felsic matrix which is continuous with the microgranite (Figures 49, 50). The breccia appears to be in steep contact with the layered gabbros and transgresses the layering. Felsic net-veining is widespread and extends for several metres into the mafic rocks where it forms flat-lying sheets and zones conformable with the layering (Figure 50). Within the breccia zone there are trains of even-textured basaltic fragments which represent dykes in various stages of disintegration, and in one instance a dyke in microgranite may be followed into a train of blocks (Figure 49). A few fragments of dolerite have rounded, lobate, fine-grained selvedges against the felsic matrix, suggesting that there was limited co-existence of mafic and felsic magmas.

From the rocks of the Harris Bay localities it is clear that the emplacement of hot, mafic material into earlier granitic rocks resulted in generation of rheomorphic silicic magma, with the formation of intrusion breccias and felsic net-veining, a phenomenon that is common throughout the central complexes of the Palaeogene volcanic districts (e.g. Blake *et al.*, 1965). Return to the Abhainn Rangail bridge and walk upstream for 150 m.

Figure 49. Zone of intrusion breccia at the contact of the Western Granite with bytownite gabbro of the Western Layered Intrusion, Locality 4.17, East end of Harris Bay. The line of dark blocks is a dyke broken up in the remobilised acid (felsic) matrix. (Photo: Emeleus/BGS © NERC)

Figure 50. Layered gabbro in the Western Layered Intrusion intruded by rheomorphic felsic veins derived from remobilisation of the earlier Western Granite in this area. The felsic magma has been channelled along planes of weakness provided by the layered structures. Locality 4.17, east side of Harris Bay. Scale: hammer shaft 30 cm.

Locality 4.18 [NM 3450 9557]

Abhainn Rangail – peridotite breccia in Central Intrusion, with chromite seams

At the junction of the Abhainn Rangail with the Allt Lag Sleitir, which enters from the north-west, ultrabasic breccias belonging to the Central Intrusion crop out in the stream bed (Figure 40a). The breccias consist of angular and subangular blocks of peridotite and feldspathic peridotite in a feldspathic peridotite matrix containing thin seams of black, lustrous chromite. They were interpreted by Wadsworth (1961) to have formed at fault-scarps in a magma chamber and by Donaldson (1975) to be intrusive breccias. Walk due north for 800 m to regain the road near Hugh's Brae [NM 345 964]. Return to Kinloch (c. 8 km), examining Localities 4.9 and 4.10 on the way (see above).

Excursion 5
The Canna Lava Formation in north-west Rum

HIGHLIGHTS

This excursion is concerned with the lavas and conglomerates of the Canna Lava Formation, the youngest manifestations of volcanicity on Rum, apart from a few dykes that intrude the lavas. The lavas crop out in north-west Rum (Figure 2) and are at some distance from Kinloch. Examination of the major localities involves a walk of over 20 km, climbing to about 500 m altitude near Orval (at [NM 334 993]) and about 300 m on Bloodstone Hill [NG 315 006]. Shorter alternatives are indicated.

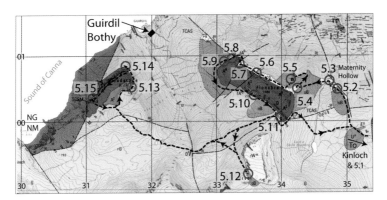

Figure 51. Geological map of the Canna Lava Formation on Fionchra and Bloodstone Hill, north-west Rum. Excursion 5, for locality 5.1 and Kinloch road see Figure 33. (See pp. 148-49 for full key; based on SNH 1:20,000 solid geology map; © SNH.)

Table 2: The Canna Lava Formation on Rum	
Orval Member	Thick flows of basaltic hawaiite, some feldspar-phyric. Overlies Western Granite and flows of the Lower Fionchra Member.
Guirdil Member	Two flows of tholeiitic andesite ('icelandite'), each underlain by lenses of fluviatile conglomerate. Overlies flows of the Upper Fionchra Member, the Main Ring Fault, the Western Granite and sandstones of the Torridon Group.
Upper Fionchra Member	Flows of tholeiitic basaltic andesite underlain by fluviatile conglomerates of variable thickness. Overlies flows of the Lower Fionchra Member, the Main Ring Fault, the Western Granite and sandstones of the Torridon Group.
Lower Fionchra Member	Flows of olivine basalt and rare basaltic hawaiite flows. Underlain by lenses of fluviatile conglomerate up to 50 m in thickness. The member rests on a weathered surface of Western Granite on Orval (Black, 1952) and sandstones of the Torridon Group, and overlies the Main Ring Fault.

Take the Harris track to Malcolm's Bridge [NM 3596 9937], as for Excursion 4. Then follow the path on the east side of the stream for about 1 km to the north and west-north-west. Exposure is poor, but after about 700 m scattered exposures of feldspathic peridotite give way to gabbroic rocks and then to intrusion breccia (Figure 33 and 51).

Locality 5.1 [NM 354 998]

North-west of Malcolm's Bridge – contact between Central Intrusion and Western Granite

Intrusion breccia is present at the contact between microgranite to the west and later mafic rocks of the Central Intrusion. A large peridotite plug also cuts the microgranite hereabouts but exposure is poor. Leave the path where 'fords' are indicated on the OS 1:25,000 map [NM 351 999] and walk about 350 m slightly west of north to the west side of the lochan near a flat-topped hill ('West Minishal' [NG 349 003]). The hill consists of several near-horizontal olivine basalt flows belonging to the Lower Fionchra Member of the Canna Lava Formation. The lochan is on the line of a fault that marks the eastern limit to the formation on Rum.

Locality 5.2 [NG 3475 0064]

'West Minishal' – conglomerates containing clasts
derived from central complex

Lavas overlie a thick (*c*.65m) fluviatile conglomerate that crops out on
the steep, north-facing hillside to the north-west of the lochan. Coarse,
unbedded conglomerate on the upper slopes contains boulders and cobbles
of gneiss, amphibolite, red sandstone, tholeiitic basalt (including
amygdaloidal rocks) and dolerite, and additionally, gabbro, altered
bytownite troctolite, microgranite, porphyritic rhyodacite and other rocks
all clearly derived from the Rum Central Complex.

Locality 5.3 [NG 3472 0062]

Maternity Hollow – fluviatile conglomerates
faulted against Torridonian sandstone

Exposures at Maternity Hollow are in much finer grained rocks than at
Locality 5.2. Pebble- and granule-rich beds predominate and small logs and
other plant remains have been found here. The bedded rocks on the north
side of the stream are overlain by superficial deposits that contain similar
clasts to the Paleocene conglomerates, including pristine bytownite troctolite (in contrast to the bytownite troctolite clasts with thoroughly altered
olivines in the earlier rocks). The Paleocene deposits terminate to the east at
a fault which has brought them against Torridonian sandstone. This fault
continues south-south-east to the lochan and marks the eastern limit of the
Canna Lava Formation on Rum (Figure 51).

From Maternity Hollow, follow the stream uphill in a west-south-west
direction. Just west of the hollow, red (Torridonian) sandstone crops out on
the south side of the stream. Discontinuous exposures of conglomerate
occupy the next 100 m of the stream bed, as far as the first lava flow. This
lava, which forms a small shelf at [NG 3457 0059] is about 20 m lower than
the basal lava of West Minishal and a small fault presumably separates the
localities. Exposure is poor over the next 300 m until an east-facing,
mound-like mass of coarse conglomerate is encountered in a shallow
amphitheatre.

Locality 5.4 [NG 342 005]

East of Fionchra – varied clasts in fluviatile conglomerates; palaeovalley in lavas

The clasts in the conglomerate forming the mound are similar to those seen at localities 5.2 and 5.3, but with the addition of (altered) olivine basalt. This conglomerate is locally over 20 m thick and occupies a palaeovalley eroded in flows of the Lower Fionchra Member. To the north and south, olivine basalts form the steep sides to this valley, and the conglomerate here is clearly younger than that seen at Locality 5.3. Nearby, to the north, the lavas have shelf-like outcrops, which are commonly peat-covered. Their contact with the red Torridonian sandstone (around [NG 3438 0076]) is highly irregular, and they were evidently erupted onto a hilly sandstone landscape (Emeleus, 1985). The lavas hereabouts are cut by twin, 2 m-wide north-trending olivine basalt dykes.

Locality 5.5 [NG 341 005]

North-east side, Fionchra – hyaloclastites (including pillows) exposed in fallen blocks

The lower slopes of the steep, north-east face of Fionchra [NG 339 004] are mantled by block scree derived from hyaloclastite breccia. This breccia forms a *c.* 50 m-thick bed around the base of the hill and extends westwards to Coire na Loigh [NG 331 009] (see below). The breccia is best examined in the large blocks. It consists of small basaltic pillows and pillow fragments embedded in a comminuted, basaltic matrix (Figures 52, 53). The matrix contains shards of fresh, yellowish glass with microphenocrysts of plagioclase, pyroxene and olivine, although most of the glass has been devitrified and palagonitised. The rock is a tholeiitic basaltic andesite, similar to the flows that form the upper levels of Fionchra. The flows, hyaloclastite rocks and conglomerate of the dome belong to the Upper Fionchra Member of the Canna Lava Formation.

If desired, the excursion may now be shortened. Contour around the east end of Fionchra to the Bealach a'Bhràigh Bhig [NG 340 000]. The exposures at the bealach (Locality 5.11, see below) should be examined

81

Figure 52. Pillows in a hyaloclastite deposit at the base of the Upper Fionchra Member of the Canna Lava Formation. Locality 5.5, north-east side of Fionchra. Scale: hammer head c. 15 cm.

Figure 53. Fragments of glassy scoria-ceous basaltic andesite in hyaloclastite deposits at base of Upper Fionchra Member of the Canna Lava Formation. Near Locality 5.5, Fionchra. Scale: c. 20 cm in length.

before returning to Malcolm's Bridge by the well-marked path and thence to Kinloch. The longer excursion continues along the steep slopes on the north side of Fionchra, contouring at about 370 m altitude, where there is an ill-defined deer path just below the base of the cliffs. Exercise care, as the grassy and rubble-covered slopes may be slippery, especially in wet conditions.

Streams draining the north side of Fionchra provide transects through the lower part of the Upper Fionchra Member. About 400 m north-west of Fionchra summit, 30 m of bedded gritty and pebbly sandstone with silty partings underlies the hyaloclastite breccia, resting on red sandstone belonging to the Torridon Group.

Locality 5.6 [NG 3365 0068]

North side, Fionchra – stream section through plant-bearing silty sandstones

The finer grained rocks close to and below the deer track contain delicate leaf and stem impressions and a variety of organic remains. These remains have been used to date the deposits to 58.0 to 58.2 Ma (Jolley, 1997). Continue west-north-west, keeping at much the same level until a pronounced gully is reached after 360 m.

82

Locality 5.7 [NG 3346 0088]

North side, Fionchra – coarse fluviatile conglomerate
underlying feldspar-phyric lava

The gully exposes about 30 m of coarse fluviatile conglomerate overlain by a feldspar-phyric basaltic andesite. Boulders and cobbles of red sandstone predominate in the lower part of the section; at higher levels clasts of altered olivine basalt also appear, derived from flows of the Lower Fionchra Member. Continue north-west for a further 150 m, to Coire na Loigh.

Locality 5.8 [NG 3322 0098]

Coire na Loigh – conglomerates and lavas
faulted against Torridonian sandstone

Red sandstone (TCAS) crops out to the north of the cliff at Coire na Loigh. It is separated from the lavas and conglomerates by a north-north-west-trending fault, which defines the northerly limit of the Canna Lava Formation on Rum. To the south, columnar basaltic andesite overlies about 10 m of conglomerate. Bloodstone has been obtained from the base of the lava hereabouts.

Locality 5.9 [NG 3314 0092]

Coire na Loigh – lava with thin, glassy basal selvedge
overlying conglomerate

Some 150 m to the south-west of Locality 5.8, hyaloclastite deposits are exposed at the back of Coire na Loigh. They are separated from the underlying conglomerate (now reduced to about 2 m thickness) by some 2 m of columnar lava with a thin glassy selvedge at its base. Impersistent basalt scarps below the conglomerate and up to 400 m to the west belonging to basalt flows in the Lower Fionchra Member, and conglomerates at the base of this member, are exposed at 90 m elevation in the stream in Coire na Loigh (at [NG 3279 0131]). Nearby, steep dips in the 30 m-thick basal conglomerate and adjoining red sandstone (TCAS) are attributed to drag on the continuation of the north-north-west-trending fault noted at Locality 5.8.

There are excellent views of Bloodstone Hill [NG 315 006] from Coire na Loigh. Flat-lying lava flows overlie and are banked against featureless sandstone (Torridon Group) and, higher in the succession, two flows of tholeiitic andesite ('icelandite') of the Guirdil Member (Table 2, page 79) may be distinguished. They fill a valley eroded in earlier flows. The Bloodstone Hill outlier may be reached from Coire na Loigh by descending to about 50 m in Guirdil and ascending the steep hillside to the west, to the base of the lava crags (at Locality 5.13 [NG 3167 0066]). The relevant localities are described later.

To continue the traverse around Fionchra from Coire na Loigh, follow the lava cliff until it dies out about 100 m to the south-west. Traverse around the west end of Fionchra for about 250 m in an east-south-east direction, climbing gently to about 320 m altitude until a prominent 250 m-long cliff is reached on the south side of the hill (Figure 56). This feature is formed by a 20 m-thick tholeiitic andesite (icelandite) flow. This flow and the underlying 1–2 m of conglomerate belong to the Guirdil Member (Figures 54, 55); they overlie strongly feldspar-phyric basaltic andesite (similar to the basal flow on the east face of Bloodstone Hill and at Locality 5.7) and are banked against hyaloclastite deposits of the Upper Fionchra Member. The relationship between the hyaloclastite rocks and the feldspar-phyric flow are obscured by talus. Both are at the base of the Upper Fionchra Member succession.

Locality 5.10 [NG 3363 0038]

South side, Fionchra – lava and conglomerate
ponded against wall of hyaloclastite

Conglomerate and the flow-banded base of the tholeiitic andesite (icelandite) are well exposed towards the eastern end of the cliff (Figure 54). The clasts are broadly similar to those in previous localities, except that they include tholeiitic basaltic andesite cobbles (including strongly feldspar-phyric varieties) derived from the Upper Fionchra Member. Flow structures at the base of the lava wrap around cobbles and boulders in the irregular surface of the conglomerate and the flow has characteristic close-set, irregular jointing. The conglomerate and tholeiitic andesite die out at the east end of the cliff, where it can be verified that the lava is banked against a

84

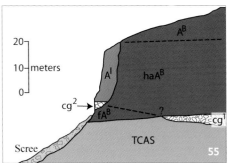

Figure 54. Fluviatile conglomerates underlying tholeiitic basaltic andesite ('icelandite') lava flow (Guirdil Member, Canna Lava Formation). Locality 5.10, south side of Fionchra. Scale: hammer shaft: 30 cm. (Photo: Emeleus/BGS © NERC)

Figure 55. Cross-section showing the relationship between the valley-filling tholeiitic basaltic andesite flow ('icelandite') (A^I) and underlying conglomerate (cg^2) to the flows of the Upper Fionchra Member and feldspar-phyric basaltic andesite (fA^B), and banked against a palaeocliff in hyaloclastite deposits (haA^B) underlain by another conglomerate (cg^1). Lower slopes are mantled by coarse talus. Locality 5.10, south side of Fionchra. Locality as for Figure 54.

steep surface formed by hyaloclastite deposits belonging to the Upper Fionchra Member (Figure 55). The tholeiitic andesite flow flooded a steep-sided valley parallel to the present hillside. Conglomerate exposed a short distance to the east-south-east of the cliff (at [NG 3366 0037]) belongs to the Upper Fionchra Member. To complete the traverse around Fionchra, continue south-east to the Bealach a'Bhràigh Bhig, at the head of Guirdil.

Locality 5.11 [NG 3395 0010]

Bealach a'Bhràigh Bhig – lava resting on rubbly microgranite surface

The tholeiitic andesite flow examined at Locality 5.10 is continued in the prominent dark, west-facing cliff about 150 m north of the bealach. It rests on a surface formed by rounded masses of microgranite considered to be *in situ*. Patchy outcrops of conglomerate occur up to 200 m west of the bealach (Figure 55) where flat-lying gritty layers have yielded plant fragments; conglomerate also crops out in the path north-west of the bealach. From the bealach it is an easy climb over basaltic andesite flows to

85

Figure 56. Western Granite crags on the north side of Orval, overlain by lava flows of the Lower Fionchra and Orval members (Canna Lava Formation) forming dark exposures towards the end of the cliff. Fionchra is in the middle distance (note the cliff of tholeiitic andesite) and the Skye Cuillin is visible on the horizon. Note the moraine-dammed lochan. Pale crags and talus in the foreground are on the Western Granite.

the summit of Fionchra, from where there are fine views of the hills in north-west Rum and Canna, with the Outer Isles in the far distance. To the north of Glen Shellesder a prominent hill is formed by a peridotite plug near Loch Sgaorishal [NG 348 022] (Excursion 6); beyond this, across the sea, are the cliffs and hills of the Skye Lava Group west of Loch Brittle and the mass of the Skye Cuillin, which dominates the skyline. The lavas in that part of Skye pre-date the Cuillin gabbros and have interbedded conglomerates that contain clasts derived from the Rum Central Complex (Williamson and Bell, 1994).

The excursion may be terminated at this point and the return to Kinloch (8 km) made by the path to Malcolm's Bridge and the road. To continue to Bloodstone Hill (3 km), follow the path west, along the northern slopes of Orval. After about 700 m, walk uphill for about 600 m in a south-east direction to the cleft visible to the east of Orval.

Locality 5.12 [NM 335 992]

Orval – classic locality where lavas were shown to rest
on weathered microgranite

Thick flows of basaltic hawaiite belonging to the Orval Member form steep
slopes and cliffs to the east (Figure 56), but at about 490 m elevation in the
cleft there is a series of thin, shelf-forming flows that may be traced up to
the low pass east of Orval (Figures 56, 57). These olivine basalt and basaltic
hawaiite flows are considered to belong to the Lower Fionchra Member
(Emeleus, 1985). Early workers on Rum had assumed that all the lavas in
north-west Rum pre-dated the Rum Central Complex since they were
thought to have been intruded and metamorphosed by the Western Granite
(Harker, 1908; Bailey, 1945). In the 1950s, however, a trench dug at the
base of the lavas hereabouts exposed lavas overlying a weathered microgranite surface (Black, 1952). This crucial evidence, together with that
provided by other exposures (e.g. Locality 5.11) and the clast content of the
conglomerates, demonstrates beyond doubt that the lavas of north west
Rum post-date the Rum Central Complex.

Figure 57. Western Granite on Ard Nev (left distance). Orval (right distance) has a capping of lavas of the Orval Member, Canna Lava Formation, on granite. Peridotite belonging to the Central Intrusion crops out in the foreground.

87

Return to the path and follow it west to the lochan at the Bealach an Dubh Bhràigh [NM 321 997], then for about 600 m across peaty ground with scattered microgranite exposures. A thick (7 m) north-north-east-trending picritic dolerite dyke may be examined where the path crosses a stream flowing north at [NM 3262 9959]. At about [NG 3155 0012] the northern (faulted) edge of the microgranite is crossed. For the next 150 m exposures are rare, although there is much loose sandstone, and sandstone crops out nearby in the headwaters of the Allt Airigh na Maith-innse [NG 3119 0006].

The low cliff at [NG 3148 0026] on Bloodstone Hill is formed by the upper of two tholeiitic andesite flows (Guirdil Member) which may be traced over much of the summit area.

Locality 5.13 [NG 317 006]

Bloodstone Hill – lavas lying on weathered sandstone, overlain by valley-fill lavas

The two tholeiitic andesite flows are well exposed in the east-facing cliffs where each is underlain by a thin, impersistent fluviatile conglomerate. The silty beds at the top of the conglomerates that separate the flows, contain plant fragments and very thin (< 2 cm) seams of poor coal. The flows fill a steep-sided palaeovalley eroded in sandstone (TCAS) and in lavas belonging to the Upper Fionchra Member. The underlying Lower Fionchra Member is up to 100 m thick, thinning rapidly to the south. These flows occupy an older palaeovalley of which only the southern (sandstone) slope remains.

The precipitous cliffs on the north-west face of Bloodstone Hill are formed by flows of the Upper Fionchra Member. The cliff edges must be avoided since close-jointed crumbling basalt, and joints, clefts and hollows masked by heather, make them hazardous. The 19th-century excavations for bloodstone have been obliterated so that the only reliable present-day source of bloodstone is in the gravel and pebbles on the beaches near the Guirdil bothy [NG 3196 0134] (Excursion 6; Locality 6.12).

Locality 5.14 [NG 3149 0082]

North end of Bloodstone Hill – lava on weathered sandstone

The basaltic andesite flows on Bloodstone Hill generally rest directly on sandstone. An accessible basal contact is exposed at 300 m elevation on the north face of the hill where lavas lie on a regolith of sandstone fragments but without any development of conglomerate. This locality may be reached directly from the summit area, although the descent is steep and there are numerous small basalt crags. An easier approach is to follow the edge of the tholeiitic andesite flows downhill from Locality 5.13 and traverse around the hillside at about 300 m elevation, noting that the basal feldspar-phyric basaltic andesite flow resembles that near Locality 5.10.

Locality 5.15 [NG 3107 0035]

West side of Bloodstone Hill – rhyodacite boulder in conglomerate

The sole exposure of fluviatile conglomerate at the base of the Upper Fionchra Member on Bloodstone Hill is somewhat inaccessible. The locality may be reached (with extreme care) along a steep, narrow goat path from the cliff top at [NG 3100 0009]. The path follows the palaeovalley contact between lava flows and sandstone. The exposure is notable for the presence of a very large (c. 2 m diameter) boulder of porphyritic rhyodacite. The return to Kinloch (c. 11 km) is along the path to the Bealach a'Bhràigh Bhig and Malcolm's Bridge. Alternatively, descend to Guirdil beach (Locality 6.11) to search for bloodstone and agate, and return to Kinloch by the path from the Guirdil bothy to Glen Shellesder, then continue east up the glen to join the Kilmory–Kinloch road (Excursion 6; Figure 51).

Excursion 6
Minishal and north-west Rum

HIGHLIGHTS

This excursion affords the opportunity to examine the north end of the Layered Centre, the major peridotite plug north of Glen Shellesder and minor intrusions cutting the Torridonian and Triassic rocks, as well as features in the sedimentary successions. The total distance is 18–20km.

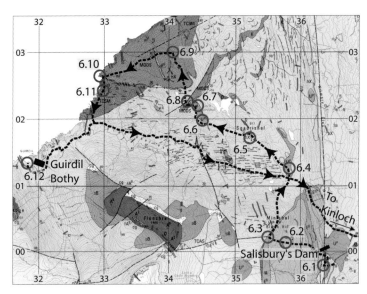

Figure 58. Geological map of the north end of the Central Intrusion, Minishal and the country around Sgaorishal and the north-west coast of Rum. Excursion 6. (See pp. 148-49 for full key; based on SNH 1:20,000 solid geology map; © SNH.)

Take the Harris road to the point where Salisbury's Dam [NM 364 999] is visible. Upstream from the dam, the Kilmory River has cut steep-sided valleys in the easily weathered mafic rocks of the Central Intrusion (Figure 58).

Locality 6.1 [NM 3639 9962]

Kilmory River – alkaline segregations in peridotite of Central Intrusion

Follow the tributary of the Kilmory River south for about 200 m from the dam to where thin, pale-coloured alkaline segregations and veins traverse crumbling peridotite. Material used for U-Pb dating (60.53 Ma) of the Central Intrusion was obtained from these veins (Pearson *et al.*, 1996; Hamilton *et al.*, 1998). Return to the dam and walk west-north-west for about 700 m across north–south-trending scarps and exposures of gabbro and peridotite in the northern extension of the Central Intrusion (Figures 2 and 58).

Locality 6.2 [NG 3583 0018]

West of Salisbury's Dam – replacement 'finger structures' in peridotite

A prominent south-east-facing scarp exposes weakly laminated and layered, pale grey feldspathic peridotite underlain by brown peridotite (Figure 59). The contact is highly irregular. Finger-like protrusions of brown peridotite penetrate, cross-cut and apparently replace the overlying feldspathic peridotite. They are excellent examples of the replacement 'finger structures' found in the peridotites of the Rum Central Complex and elsewhere (Butcher *et al.*, 1985; Robbins, 1982; Emeleus and Bell, 2005).

Locality 6.3 [NG 3550 0022]

Minishal – Main Ring Fault, sandstone and microgranite cut by peridotite

About 300 m to the west of Locality 6.2, the contact between peridotite and the microgranite and sandstone to the west is obscured in a shallow,

Figure 59. Finger structures developed where peridotite has replaced overlying, layered troctolite. East of Minishal. North end of Central Intrusion. Locality 6.2. Scale: hammer shaft 30 cm.

north–south depression. Indurated baked sandstone and microgranite are exposed in a north-north-east-trending scarp on the east face of Minishal. Careful examination of the exposures in the scarp reveals a continuous passage from sandstone through brecciated sandstone and microgranite to microgranite at the southern end. This faulted contact is part of the Main Ring Fault and it has been heavily overprinted by thermal metamorphism due to emplacement of the Central Intrusion (Hughes *et al.*, 1957; cf. Black, 1954).

Locality 6.4 [NG 356 002]

Path north of Minishal – peridotite plug with some layering, intruding sandstone

About 1 km to the north of Locality 6.3, the Kilmory Glen–Glen Shellesder path crosses a low col at 139 m [NG 357 001]. A very elongate peridotite plug extends north-north-west for about 600 m from a lochan just north of the path. Weakly developed centimetre-scale layering is developed in peridotite about 200 m north of the lochan. The adjoining sandstone is typically bleached and grey in colour. Continue in a north-west direction for almost 1 km, to the hill Sgaorishal [NG 3505 0195].

Locality 6.5 [NG 3523 0175]

Sgaorishal – 'fissure-breccia' in sandstone, which is baked and bleached

200 m south-south-east of the summit there is a narrow, north-north-west-trending zone of bleached and brecciated sandstone. This is one of many similar zones in northern Rum (especially on Mullach Mòr) where the sandstone has been severely baked, in some instances with the production of tridymite (now represented by quartz paramorphs) and commonly exhibiting indications of partial melting. A possible explanation is that headed dykes underlie these 'fissure breccias' (Harker, 1908; Emeleus, 1997). A thick, north-west-trending, dolerite dyke cuts sandstone on Sgaorishal summit. Continue west, skirting the southern side of Loch Sgaorishal, then take a direction slightly south of west for 400 m.

Locality 6.6 [NG 3446 0198]

'West Sgaorishal' – contact of sandstone and peridotite exposed in plug

A contact between peridotite and sandstone crops out on the west side of the line of peridotite exposures that marks the north-west-trending 'tail' of a major peridotite plug forming the summit of the unnamed, craggy hill (Locality 6.7) west of Loch Sgaorishal. The sandstone has been severely baked and partially melted, but the adjoining peridotite is fresh, with little indication of any chilling at the contact. The peridotite is intruded by a thin picrite dyke, one of the rare examples of minor intrusions cutting a peridotite or gabbro plug.

Locality 6.7 [NG 3430 0224]

'West Sgaorishal' – matrix banding and strong jointing in peridotite plug

In the vicinity of the summit (272 m) there is an excellent development of 'matrix banding' in peridotite (Dunham, 1965; Figure 60). On the north-west side of this intrusion, referred to as the West Sgaorishal Plug (Power *et al.*, 2003), the peridotite is in contact with Triassic sandstone and cornstone.

93

Figure 60. Steep matrix banding in the West Sgaorishal peridotite plug. Locality 6.7, west of Sgaorishal.

Locality 6.8 [NG 3427 0229]

'West Sgaorishal' – Triassic cornstones at peridotite contact containing chalcopyrite and malachite

The contact zone is notable for the development of areas of chalcopyrite in the peridotite, with malachite occuring in the sandstone nearby (at [NG 3422 0223]). The sulphide minerals found at this locality, and elsewhere on the margins of the plug, host platinum-group element mineralisation, which is also present in thin sulphide-rich dykes that cut the peridotite (Power *et al.*, 2003). The sandstone at this locality is part of a downfaulted strip (Figure 58); the main body of Triassic sandstone and cornstone in north-west Rum is a short distance to the north where it forms a long, low scarp that descends westward to the coast.

The Triassic Monadh Dubh Sandstone Formation of north-west Rum is about 600 m in thickness. Carbonate concretions ('cornstones') are common throughout the lower 400 m and are especially well developed in coastal exposures and low cliffs about 0.5 km north of Glen Shellesder (Figure 61; Steel, in Emeleus, 1997).

94

Figure 61. Triassic Monadh Dubh Sandstone Formation (MODS) overlying Torridon Group, Aultbea Formation (TCSM). Cornstones in the basal Triassic beds form a white band half-way up cliff and permeate joints and bedding planes in the underlying Torridonian sandstones at the base of the cliff for up to 3 m. Thin basaltic sheets cut the Torridonian rocks. Locality 6.10, about 1 km north of Glen Shellesder, north-west Rum. (Photo: Emeleus/BGS © NERC)

Locality 6.9 [NG 3404 0300]

Monadh Dubh – plant and ostracod remains in Triassic silty sandstones

Poorly preserved plant remains and ostracods have been recovered from silty sandstones belonging to the topmost Allt Dubh Member of the Monadh Dubh Sandstone Formation at this locality. About 300 m to the south-south-west the sandstones are cut by 'fissure breccias' and by a thick, badly weathered dyke of microgabbro. Numerous north-west- to north-north-west-trending basalt dykes belonging to the Rum Swarm crop out along the coast between Glen Shellesder and Kilmory. Very commonly their positions are marked by clefts and breaks in the sandstone cliffs (e.g. at [NG 3326 0295]).

Locality 6.10 [NG 3301 0262]

North of Glen Shellesder – cornstones permeating brecciated Torridonian sandstone

Low cliffs close to the coast expose angular, blocky fragments of Torridonian sandstone cemented by carbonate minerals to form a breccia at the base of the Triassic succession on Rum. Carbonate has also penetrated into the underlying sandstones and is prominent in the overlying bedded deposits (Figure 61).

Locality 6.11 [NG 3300 0248]

Coast at Glen Shellesder – heavy mineral bands in Torridonian sandstone

Sandstones belonging to the Sgorr Mhòr Sandstone Member of the Aultbea Formation crop out in raised beach stacks and on the foreshore south-south-west of Locality 6.10. The beds are high in the local Torridonian succession (Figure 3); they consist of fine-grained, laminated sandstones, commonly with dense black, heavy mineral-rich layers. Soft-sediment deformation occurs in the sandstones; this is picked out by deformed dark layers. The day may be completed by taking the path from Glen Shellesder to the Guirdil bothy (which will add 2.5–3 km), or by returning up Glen Shellesder to regain the road to Kinloch.

Locality 6.12 [NG 3196 0134]

Guirdil Bothy – bloodstone and agate pebbles on the foreshore

Bloodstone pebbles are usually to be found in gravels on the beach below the Guirdil bothy, together with small, finely banded pebbles of white agate. The return to Kinloch (about 9 km) is most easily made by retracing one's steps and following the path through Glen Shellesder rather than undertaking the long climb up Guirdil to Bealach a'Bhràigh Bhig and then to Malcolm's Bridge (see Excursion 5).

Excursions 7, 8 and 9

The Southern Mountains and Dibidil

by E. P. Holohan, V. R. Troll and C. H. Emeleus

Exploration of the highly variable and structurally complex geology of the spectacular Southern Mountains may be undertaken from Kinloch Castle. Alternatively, one may use the refurbished and re-roofed 'open bothy', maintained by the Scottish Mountain Bothy Association for one or more overnights (see p. 5 for items needed for the bothies). This bothy [3930 9275] is situated in Dibidil about a hundred metres west of the mouth of Dibidil River. On this basis, we provide below a number of suggested routes around the Southern Mountains. Each route has various optional or additional branches that the reader can explore upon consideration of time available, weather conditions, and starting and end points for the day (i.e. accommodation in bothy vs. castle). The 1:25,000 'Explorer' Ordnance Survey map (with cliffs marked) is absolutely necessary for these excursions.

SAFETY NOTE

Several large streams cross the path between Dibidil and Kinloch. The lag time on the island from rainfall to streamflow is very short (a few hours), and if rainfall is heavy or lengthy, these streams consequently swell very rapidly into raging torrents that may prove impassable and can be fatal if attempted. If presented with such a problem while walking along the Dibidil path, the best solution is usually to detour upstream away from the path. Once a suitably safe fording point is found, cross the stream and walk back down beside the stream to rejoin the path. If still in Dibidil before the onset of bad weather, bear in mind that it is also possible to return to Kinloch by walking up to the head of Glen Dibidil to Bealach an Oir (the col between Askival and Trollaval). However, this option is not recommended in poor weather conditions, especially with low cloud. If the visibility is good, from the bealach contour through the screes on the lower slopes of Askival, to the west side of Hallival, then on to the col between Barkeval and Hallival. From that col walk down into Coire Dubh and take the path from the hydro-electric dam to Kinloch. The journey time for this route is perhaps slightly longer (3.0–3.5 hours) than by going along the Dibidil path. Alternatively, if it were essential to get back to Kinloch and visibility was bad, it would be possible to walk down into Atlantic Corrie, then to the south end of the Long Loch and follow along near the west side of the loch to the 'whaleback' (Excursion 4), reaching the Harris–Kinloch road north of Locality 4.4. (The total distance for this roundabout route from Dibidil to Kinloch is about 13 km.)

Kinloch – Allt nam Bà – Beinn nan Stac – Lower Glen Dibidil

HIGHLIGHTS

This excursion focuses on the tectonics of the Main Ring Fault system around Beinn nan Stac and lower Glen Dibidil. Key relationships in the lower slopes of Beinn nan Stac provide evidence of pre-caldera uplift and folding followed by subsidence. The upper slopes and peak of Beinn nan Stac host deposits of high-energy debris and pyroclastic flows, interpreted as part of a caldera-infill succession. Along the way, the marginal gabbro to the Layered Centre is examined and its post-Main Ring Fault emplacement verified. The spectacular roof contact between the Stage 1 pyroclastic and sedimentary rocks and the Stage 2 ultrabasic magma chamber rocks is inspected. Superb views across to the Southern Mountains (Figure 63) and to Eigg, Muck and beyond are obtained from Beinn nan Stac peak. Exposed in the Dibidil River are relationships between an enigmatic (Am Màm-type) intrusive breccia, intrusive porphyritic rhyodacite and the deformed basement rocks. Furthermore, Dibidil Cove offers the chance to put a finger on the razor-sharp Main Ring Fault surface between uplifted gneiss and pulverised Torridonian mudstones.

The distance covered on this route is about 16–18 km, if all exposures are examined. The maximum altitude reached is 546 m on Beinn nan Stac, but the total height climbed is probably nearer 800 m.

About 130 m south-east of the White House (Reserve Office) in Kinloch, a rough signposted path (pony track) leads southwards to Dibidil and Papadil from the inland splay of the road between the castle and the pier. The path climbs steadily south-south-east over wet, partly peat-covered, sandstone slabs, and after just over 1 km from Kinloch, levels off at about 200 m altitude.

99

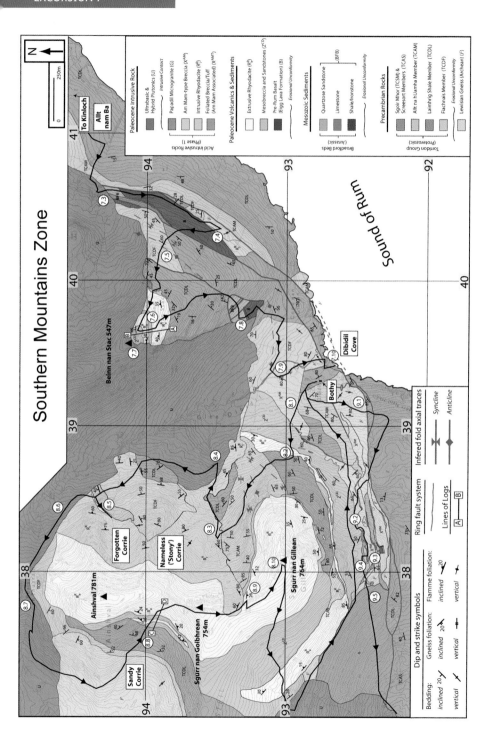

Southern Mountains Zone

Paleocene Intrusive Rock
- Ultrabasic & Hybrid Plutonics (U)
- Papadil Microgranite (G)
  - *Intrusive Contact*
- Am Mam-type Breccia (X^AM)
- Intrusive Rhyodacite (R^R)
- Foliated Breccia/Tuff (Am Mam Associated) (X^AMT)

Acid Intrusive Rocks (Phase 1)

Paleocene Volcanics & Sediments
- Extrusive Rhyodacite (R^R)
- Mesobreccia and Sandstones (Z^CV)
- Pre-Rum Basalt (Eigg Lava Formation) (B)
  - *Erosional Unconformity*

Mesozoic Sediments
- Quartzose Sandstone
- Limestone
- Shale/Ironstone
  (BFB)
  Erosional Unconformity

Broadford Beds (Jurassic)

Precambrian Rocks
- Sgòir Mhòr (TCSM) & Screesort Members (TCAS)
- Allt na hUamha Member (TCAM)
- Laimhrig Shale Member (TCDL)
- Fiachnais Member (TCDF)
  Erosional Unconformity
- Lewisian Gneiss (Archean) (LF)

Torridon Group (Proterozoic)

Sound of Rum

Bedding:
inclined 20 / vertical

Dip and strike symbols

Gneiss foliation:
inclined 20 / vertical

Flamme foliation:
inclined 20 / vertical

Infered fold axial traces
- Syncline
- Anticline

Ring fault system

Lines of Logs
A —— B

To Kinloch
Allt nam Ba

Sandy Corrie
Sgùrr nan Goibhrean 754m
Ainshval 781m
Forgotten Corrie
Nameless ('Stony') Corrie
Sgùrr nan Gillean 764m
Beinn nan Stac 547m
Dibidil Cove
Bothy

Locality 7.1 [NM 4095 9670]

Allt na h-Uamha – magmatic sediments

Continue south to Allt na h-Uamha (Figure 26) where a block moraine occupies the valley. Many of the blocks originated from the troctolites and peridotites that form the Hallival–Askival ridge, and so contain good examples of mineral and textural layering and associated sedimentary structures (graded layers, slump folding, etc.). A few metres upstream, badly weathered Marginal Gabbro crops out in the stream banks. Rare, thin felsic sheets, here originating from melting of the adjacent sandstones (cf. Excursions 2, 3), can be seen. South of the stream, the track skirts a prominent cliff of indurated, splintery siltstone. The cliff is formed of a lens-like body of uplifted Laimhrig Shale Member (TCDL) between the Main Ring Fault and the Marginal Gabbro (Bailey, 1945).

Locality 7.2 [NM 41 / 963]

Welshman's Rock – a doming-related ?slide

Continue south along the track for about 1 km, to the highest point on the path. Along the way, note gently north-west- or west-dipping strata of the Allt Mòr na h-Uamha Member (TCAM) which are cut by rare thin basaltic dykes trending radially to the igneous centre at about N 70° W. About 250 m east of the path is Welshman's Rock (Figure 29), a prominent 'whale-back' exposure of Torridonian rocks. If time permits, confirm that these are mainly composed of coarse, thickly bedded feldspathic sandstones akin to the Scresort Sandstone Member (TCAS). Bedding here strikes roughly east–west and dips to the south, in contrast to the general north-north-east strike and west-north-west dip outside the Main Ring Fault. The boundary between Welshman's Rock and its surroundings is an eastward-inclined normal fault (dipping at c. 35°). Downward slip off the updomed roof of the

Opposite page
Figure 62. Geological map of the Southern Mountains Zone. Based on SNH 1:20,000 solid geology map (© SNH), but extensively revised by E. Holohan and M.

Errington. Excursions 7, 8 and part of 9. For localities 7.1 and 7.2 see Figure 26, and for all of Excursion 9 see Figure 71 (see pp. 148-49 for full key).

early felsic magma body has been invoked to explain the emplacement of Welshman's Rock, the structurally similar block at Mullach Ard (Emeleus, 1997), and possibly also the Torridonian rocks outside the Main Ring Fault to the south of Dibidil around Loch Dubh an Sgòir (Nicholson, 1992). An alternative interpretation may be that these downthrown blocks are related to movements on the major Camasunary fault system, the trace of which passes close to the east side of the island (Figure 2).

Locality 7.3 [NM 4093 9424]

Allt nam Bà – margins of a ultrabasic magma chamber and evidence for subsidence on the Main Ring Fault

After another kilometre along the path, descend to the ford at Allt nam Bà (Figure 62); note that below the ford the stream has excavated a deep gorge along a Palaeogene dyke. (*Caution – the sandstone slabs in this stream may be slippery; do not cross here if the stream is in flood. Continue up stream and find a safe point.*) From the path at Allt nam Bà ford and other points here, there are good views of the prominent cliff line that defines the north-eastern side of Beinn nan Stac. Composed of baked siltstones and sandstones belonging to the Diabaig Formation, these crags are situated next to and partially roof the Marginal Gabbro and the layered ultrabasic intrusions. Walk up the southern side of the stream for about 250 m, and observe the gradual increase in the west-north-west dip of the sandstone from about 25° to over 45° (north of the stream, dips of 70° occur close to the Marginal Gabbro). At Locality 7.3a [NM 4071 9446] (Figure 62), westerly-trending basaltic dykes cut bleached, thermally metamorphosed sandstone. On the western side of a small ridge the sandstone appears to have become partly mobilised, since the basalt dykes are broken into blocks surrounded by a felsic matrix derived from sandstone. The ridge probably lies immediately outside the Main Ring Fault, which is here locally transgressed by the Marginal Gabbro.

Fifty to seventy metres to the west, the Allt nam Bà flows through a small, steep-sided valley east of a small waterfall in Marginal Gabbro. About halfway between the waterfall and Locality 7.3a, there is a low ridge that resembles a ruined, overgrown drystone wall (Locality 7.3b; [NM 4060 9436]). This exposure contains assemblages of high-temperature calc-silicate minerals (Hughes, 1960b). About 50 m to the south, exposures of marble occur on a low, east-facing cliff. A further 250–300 m south of the Allt nam Bà waterfall, on the north-east slopes of Beinn nan Stac, sheared marble with fossils of probable Jurassic age crops out (Locality 7.3c; [NM 4049 9402]; Figure 62; Smith, 1985). The presence of Mesozoic limestone inside the Main Ring Fault proves that a phase of downward movement, subsequent to an initial uplift phase (cf. Summary of Geology), was associated with this major Paleocene structure.

Locality 7.4 [NM 4033 9343]

Lower south-east flank of Beinn nan Stac – Paleocene basalt lavas and Lewisian gneiss slivers in the Main Ring Fault zone

Without losing height, traverse from Locality 7.3c in a southerly and south-south-west direction along the south east side of Beinn nan Stac. After about 300 m, exposures of fine grained, sheared, microporphyritic basalt occur; these form a north-north-east-trending zone up to 70 m in width, parallel to and inside the Main Ring Fault (Figure 62). The basalt is believed to belong to the Paleocene Eigg Lava Formation. The boundary between the lavas and the gneiss is a fault that accommodated later caldera subsidence ('Central Ring Fault' – Smith, 1985). Immediately to the east is a parallel strip of Lewisian gneiss that extends at least as far north as [NM 4040 9365], where it is adjacent to north-east-dipping exposures of Fiachanis Gritty Sandstone (TCDF) and Laimhrig Shale (TCDL). The gneiss, which is excellently exposed at [NM 4033 9343] in a low, 'whaleback' ridge just south of the stream, shows signs of severe thermal metamorphism. It is pervaded by small pockets and fingers of felsic material and has evidently undergone a degree of partial melting. The Outer Main Ring Fault strand, upon which the tilted slice of gneiss, sandstone (TCDF), and siltstone (TCDL) was uplifted, crosses the low ground along the south-east edge of the gneiss 'whaleback'. Small, undeformed intrusions of rhyodacite occur between the gneiss and sheared basalt hereabouts, and so 'stitch' the faults.

OPTIONS:

From Locality 7.4 either proceed north-west towards the summit of Beinn nan Stac, to inspect more closely the uplifted Torridonian beds, and

Paleocene breccia and rhyodacite bodies that overlie but are cross-cut by the ultrabasic Layered Centre (Figures 8, 62), or, alternatively, one can follow the south-west course of the Main Ring Fault, to rejoin the Dibidil path near Cnoc nan Gillean [NM 3980 9292], and continue on to lower Glen Dibidil or Papadil.

Locality 7.5 [NM 4004 9403]

Beinn nan Stac – folded and tilted Torridonian rocks

If Beinn nan Stac is to be visited, go first to Locality 7.5a, where baked siltstones and sandstones form the cliff above the Marginal Gabbro. At the base of the cliff, the gabbro is separated from indurated sedimentary rocks by a thin zone of hybrid rocks containing acicular amphibole (after hypersthene, which may occur as relict areas) and plagioclase. Unusually, the gabbro has a sharp, chilled margin against the hybrid rocks (Greenwood *et al.*, 1990). Return to the north-east edge of the mountain and continue westwards toward the summit of Beinn nan Stac. Note the gradual change from thin-bedded or laminated siltstones (TCDL) to the coarser, grittier, and more thickly bedded sandstones (with subordinate laminated siltstone layers) of the older Fiachanis Gritty Sandstone Member (TCDF). Bedding dip angles fluctuate considerably along the way, but bedding strike is usually north-east. The fluctuation of bedding dip angles and younging directions (as given by cross bedding in the sandstone), and the westward change from sandstone to younger siltstone reflect the folded and outward (eastward) tilted nature of the Torridonian strata hereabouts. Such uplift, tilting and folding of the Torridonian beds inside the Main Ring Fault system probably relate to forceful emplacement of the early felsic magma body. At Locality 7.5b [NM 4013 9395], about 250 m upslope from the first Torridonian exposures encountered below, coarse sandstone abruptly changes to well-laminated siltstone (TCDL) of a markedly different bedding orientation. The brecciated contact between the two lithologies is a fault that dips steeply to the west; the fault is visible, but very difficult to access, in the cliffs below. Over the next 50 m upslope, the bedding orientation of the well-laminated siltstones (TCDL) gradually changes from north-east strike and south-east dip to north-west strike and south-west dip, and so defines a south-west-plunging antiform (Figure 62).

Locality 7.6 [NM 3977 9405]

Peak of Beinn nan Stac – a volcano-sedimentary succession?

Continue climbing toward the summit while keeping close to the cliffs until a contact between increasingly brecciated but laminated rocks of the Laimhrig Shale Member and a clast-supported mesobreccia is reached. This contact is quite undulose, locally cutting down into the underlying silt-stone by several metres, e.g. at [NM 39912 93881]. The mesobreccia is dominated by clasts derived from the Laimhrig Shale Member, but pieces of coarser sandstone belonging to the Fiachanis Gritty Sandstone Member are also present. Though long thought to have formed through gas-driven subterranean explosive brecciation (Hughes, 1960a), evidence at exposures upslope and elsewhere (cf. Localities 8.5, 8.8, 9.4) shows that the mesobreccia is sedimentary in origin. This contact here probably represents a buried palaeotopography upon which the breccias were deposited, possibly as scree.

Rhyodacite overlies the mesobreccia, but exposure of the contact is restricted to the north-east flank of Beinn nan Stac [NM 39938 93976]. Elsewhere, a distinctive 5–15 m-wide zone of grass obscures it. Mesobreccia may therefore exist unexposed all along the base of the rhyodacite, or pinch out laterally (as depicted on Figure 62), in which case rhyodacite may sit directly on the Laimhrig Shale Member. Where seen on the north-east side, the rhyodacite is not obviously chilled at the basal contact against the mesobreccia. Rhyodacite and mesobreccia interfinger, and may even be somewhat gradational through lithic tuff. Two concordant but discontinuous tuff lenses occur in the rhyodacite within 1 m of the basal contact, which dips at about 50° to the west. In the rhyodacite outcrops just upslope from the contact, abundant fiamme are visible as lumpy, lenticular, or streaky features that weather proud of the host rock and/or are of different colour to it. As also seen in the Northern Marginal Zone (see Excursion 2), the fiamme define a foliation roughly concordant to the basal contact.

Continue directly upslope until the rhyodacite is found in sharp contact with overlying mesobreccia containing abundant sandstone clasts. At [NM 39770 94004] this mesobreccia grades and fines upslope, firstly into a gravelly sandstone with strong pebble alignment, and then into a coarse sandstone. More rhyodacite crops out just upslope, and its sharp unchilled basal contact against the underlying mesobreccia and sandstone is visible in

105

the adjacent cliffs on the north-east flank of Beinn nan Stac. (NB: exercise extreme caution if attempting to examine this contact here.) The meso-breccia-sandstone body is also exposed along strike around the south-west side of Beinn nan Stac; it maps out as a discrete layer sandwiched between two rhyodacite sheets. At [NM 39620 93970] on the south-east side, a very similar gradational upward transition from mesobreccia, through gravelly clast-aligned sandstone, to a lithic-rich rhyodacite basal zone, may also be (more easily) observed.

Fiamme in the upper rhyodacite sheet in the Beinn nan Stac summit area are folded locally, possibly due to rheomorphic flow, and at least one exposure near the top of the sheet [NM 39659 94028] shows distinct white- and black-weathering fiamme types. Mesobreccia, locally containing abundant basalt clasts, overlies the upper rhyodacite sheet and forms the peak of Beinn nan Stac (550 m OD; [NM 3963 9409]). Intercalated with this mesobreccia are smooth-weathering zones of pale-grey, massive, well-sorted, quartzose sandstone. Though somewhat brecciated, this sandstone bears a striking resemblance to the distinctive 'epiclastic sandstone' found just below the extrusive rhyodacite sheets of Cnapan Breaca and Meall Breac in the Northern Marginal Zone (Excursion 2), and so possibly offers a means of correlation, although the successions differ in detail. Like the ignimbrite and breccias of the Northern Marginal Zone, the Beinn nan Stac succession probably represents the lower part of a caldera-volcano's infill; evidence for structural subsidence is seen at Localities 7.4 and 7.7. Whereas fiamme foliations and bedding contacts dip to the west on the north-east flank of Beinn nan Stac, they generally dip to the north-west or north on the south-west side (Figure 62). This pattern may reflect a roughly north-west-trending palaeovalley in which the sediments and pyroclastic material accumulated. Such an interpretation has also been proposed for a very similar pattern of fiamme foliations, bedding, and base contacts at the south end of Meall Breac (Excursion 2, Locality 2.10; Troll et al., 2000).

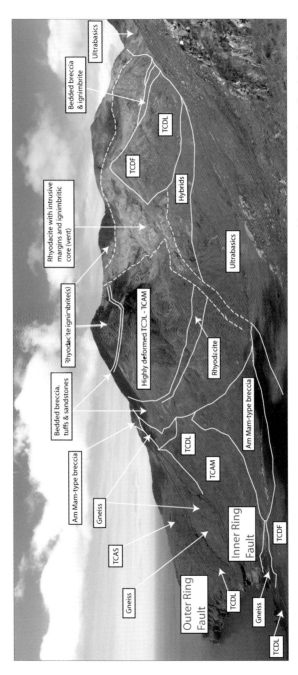

Figure 63 Panorama and geological outline of the lower south-west side of Glen Dibidil and the Sgurr nan Gillean–Ainshval Ridge, viewed from the south-east side of Beinn nan Stac (cf. Figure 64).

107

Locality 7.7 [NM 3693 9410]

Views from Beinn nan Stac

The precipitous peak of Beinn nan Stac offers spectacular views down into the depths of the glacial Glen Dibidil, across the corries and peaks of the Southern Mountains, and out over Eigg and Muck to the Scottish Highlands beyond. It is also a good vantage point from which to gain an overview of the geology of the Southern Mountains and its influence on the landscape. To the north and north-west, note the distinctive stepped form and brownish-weathering colour of Trollaval, Askival, the Askival plateau, and Hallival, where the ultrabasic and basic layered rocks predominate. Forming the skyline from north-west to south-west is the Ainshval to Sgurr nan Gillean ridge (Figure 63), the less-structured looking grey rocks of which are very similar to those of Beinn nan Stac (i.e. rhyodacites, breccias and Torridonian sandstones). Note the change in vegetation and soil from these quartz-feldspar dominated rhyodacites, breccias and Torridonian sandstones of Beinn nan Stac, Sgurr nan Gillean and Ainshval to the olivine-pyroxene-plagioclase-dominated basic and ultrabasic rocks of the Beinn nan Stac to Askival ridge, the north-east flank and headwall of Glen Dibidil, and the corrie to the north-east of Beinn nan Stac. To the south lie the waters of the Sound of Rum, and across these to the south-east is the Isle of Eigg. Eigg's geology comprises south-west-tilted layers of basalt lavas that sit unconformably upon Jurassic and Cretaceous sedimentary rocks. One also has a great view of the sinuous light-coloured ridge formed by the Sgurr of Eigg pitchstone on the southern end of Eigg. The Sgurr of Eigg Pitchstone Formation is thought to be the weathering-resistant infill (lavas and/or pyroclastic flow deposits, and some underlying fluvial sedimentary rocks) of a Paleocene palaeovalley, in which a long-vanished river once meandered across and cut down into the basaltic lavas (Emeleus, 1997; Hudson and Allwright, 2003).

Locality 7.8 [NM 3988 9341]

Lower south-west flank of Beinn nan Stac – subsided slivers of Mesozoic and Paleocene rocks

Taking care not to stray too close to the high cliff edges, descend from Beinn nan Stac peak in a south-east direction along the south-west-facing flank of the mountain. Pass the base of the rhyodacite and continue to walk south-eastward down over the many exposures of Laimhrig Shale Member (TCDL) that pepper this side of the mountain. Note that further evidence of brecciation and folding (including fold hinges) is present in many of these exposures. At [NM 39882 93411], descend into a horseshoe-shaped grassy area that is delimited by 40–50° sloping 'walls' of laminated siltstone (TCDL) (Figure 62). Within this grassy area are some exposures of buff-weathering, massive, well-sorted grey sandstone. A little further downslope there is an exposure of coarsely crystalline marble [NM 3983 9337]. Still

Figure 61. North-east side of Glen Dibidil with geological outline, viewed from the lower south east side of Sgurr nan Gillean.

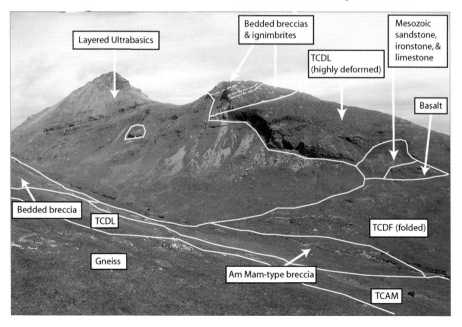

further downslope [NM 3975 9330] is an elongate exposure of ironstone – a dense, dark, and very fine-grained rock that weathers to give an extremely distinctive, splintery or flaky, rusted appearance (like the hull of an old ship). A few metres north of the ironstone, at [NM 39749 93336], are exposures of beige-weathering, well-sorted, light-grey sandstone that is very similar to that seen just below the Torridonian siltstone 'walls' upslope. This sandstone, the crystalline limestone and the ironstone are believed to be Mesozoic in age and, like the fossiliferous rocks seen south of Allt nam Bà (Locality 7.3), are considered to be downfaulted remnants of the Jurassic Broadford Beds on Skye (Smith, 1985; Emeleus, 1997). About 20 m south of the ironstone is a large mass of basalt [NM 39773 93236]. Apart from scattered vesicles, textural evidence for the exact original nature of the basalt is hard to find, but like the basalt found in the sliver zone of the south-east side of Beinn nan Stac (Locality 7.4), it is regarded as a downfaulted remnant of the Paleocene Eigg Lava Field (Emeleus, 1997). Two faults inclined at around 40° N and 50° E respectively exist between the 'walls' of siltstone (TCDL) and the slivers of Mesozoic and Paleocene rocks. Though the exact mechanisms of their emplacement are unclear, these slivers provide further evidence for subsidence inside the Main Ring Fault system.

Locality 7.9 [NM 3934 9307]

Dibidil River – 'intrusive tuffs'

From Locality 7.8 walk south or south-west for about 100–200 m until the Dibidil path is reached just to the north or north-west of Cnoc nan Gillean. Follow the path down towards the ford on the Dibidil River [NM 3934 9307]. To the south and south-west, the ground crossed before the river presents few exposures, but north of the path there are several aligned exposures of coarse grey sandstone (TCDF). A brief inspection of cross-bedding in these exposures will reveal that the beds are inclined to the north or north-east, and are upright, younging away from the river. Metre-scale plunging folds can also be seen, as at [NM 39414 93114], and the beds seem to define a tilted anticline as a whole. Take time to look back towards Beinn nan Stac at the dramatic arcuate cliff line formed of Torridonian beds with a rhyodacite and breccia cap. The base of the cliff marks the position of the gabbro bordering the Layered Centre. Inclined ridges, corresponding to layers of gabbro and peridotite, stretch from Askival across the north-east side of the glen, and up to the overarching roof-like cliffs of Beinn nan Stac, where they appear truncated (Figures 8, 64). This vista has long been considered a superb but rare cross-sectional view of the roof and sidewalls of an ultrabasic magma chamber (Emeleus, 1997).

At Dibidil ford [NM 39335 93065] is an unusual intrusive breccia, the matrix of which envelops clasts of sandstone, dolerite, gabbro and gneiss up to several metres in diameter. The breccia matrix commonly appears particulate or tuff-like. It contains euhedral crystals of plagioclase similar to those in the rhyodacite, and numerous lobate mafic inclusions. Intrusive rhyodacite, also with abundant lobate mafic inclusions, occurs about 50 m upstream of the ford. It is unclear if the rhyodacite intrudes the breccia or vice versa. A few metres further upstream from the rhyodacite are mesobreccia and more coherent siltstone (TCDL). Beyond these the river runs over the gabbros and peridotites of the Layered Centre. Good examples of intrusive breccia veining country rock are visible next to the waterfall 100–150 m downstream of the ford at [NM 39400 92946]. Here polished outcrops of gneiss and intrusive breccia are usually accessible, unless the water is very high. The gneiss here displays brittle 'domino faulting' deformation akin to that in the folded Torridonian beds (e.g. in Coire Dubh – Excursion 2), but the intrusive breccia is undeformed.

Sandstone (TCDF) is exposed a short distance downstream of the waterfall, at [NM 39435 92925] on the north-east side of the river. Bedding is oriented very similarly to that in the sandstone exposures a little further up the valley, just north of the path, so the rock is most likely *in situ*. A dyke-like rhyodacite body chills sharply against the sandstone on one side, but grades into rock very like the intrusive breccia matrix on the other. On the south-west side of the river, along strike of the rhyodacite-sandstone contact, a similar transition from rhyodacite into intrusive breccia matrix is visible just below the river-bank [NM 39408, 92946] (Figure 62). Downstream of these two points, there is no intrusive breccia or rhyodacite exposed on either side of the river. The rhyodacite seems to be marginal to the intrusive breccia body (at least locally), and so a close temporal association between the two lithologies is likely. In the Southern Mountains Zone, this intrusive breccia has previously been termed 'intrusive tuff' or 'tuffisite' (Hughes, 1960a); however, its lithological features, internal structure, structural position and timing of emplacement are very similar to the Am Màm intrusive breccia of the Northern Marginal Zone.

Locality 7.10 [NM 3947 9374]

Dibidil foreshore – a ring fault exposed

Continue to walk downstream along the north-east side of the river. After *c*. 100 m, gneiss crops out a few tens of metres upstream of where the Dibidil river plunges into the sea. A few small exposures of sandstone (TCDF) appear in the small burn north-east of the gneiss here. Like the exposures further upstream, this sandstone probably youngs away from the gneiss along the river, and so the boundary is likely to be the original erosional unconformity. Further downstream, a very sharp linear boundary between banded gneiss and intensely folded and brecciated siltstone (TCDL) is found on the foreshore next to the mouth of the Dibidil river [NM 39466 93744]. This is one of the very few places on Rum where the Main Ring Fault surface (or a splay of which) is exposed such that one can 'place a finger on it'. The fault surface is a < 30 cm-wide zone of comminuted siltstone (TCDL) and gneiss, and is inclined at about 60° to the north-west. The net displacement on the fault is reverse, with gneiss in the hanging wall

Figure 65. Siltstones of the Torridon Group (TCDL) brought against Lewisian Gneiss (right) on the Main Ring Fault (by hammer). Scale: hammer shaft *c*. 30 cm. Dibidil foreshore (Locality 7.10).

having been uplifted to its current position against the outward-tilted siltstone in the footwall (Figure 65). From here the fault is traceable north-east through a gully that runs upslope east of Cnoc nan Gillean toward the south-east edge of Beinn nan Stac. The fault may also be traced south-west across Dibidil Cove, to where gently inclined Torridonian strata (TCAS) abut against a ridge of gneiss. Upon crossing over to the foreshore immediately west of the Dibidil river, examine the small (1–2 m-wide) bodies of breccia that 'cut' the shaly beds here (TCDL). Note also that numerous undeformed basaltic sheets and dykes cut the gneiss and siltstone, and so post-date the main brecciation and folding phase(s) associated with the Main Ring Fault.

OPTIONS:

If desired at this point, a return to Kinloch may be made along the footpath (2–3 hours). Alternatively, one can overnight in the bothy (see above) and use the following or subsequent days to explore other areas of the Southern Mountains.

Excursion 8

Lower Glen Dibidil – Nameless and Forgotten corries – Upper Glen Dibidil – Sandy Corrie – Sgurr nan Gillean

HIGHLIGHTS

Designed to take advantage of the excellent three-dimensional exposure afforded by the rugged topography around Sgurr nan Gillean and Ainshval, this excursion includes closer inspection of the volcanism, tectonism and intrusions associated with stages 1 and 2 of the Rum volcano. Evidence for the composite intrusion and subsequent fragmentation of rhyodacite and basaltic magmas in a feeder system to surface eruptions is examined in Nameless Corrie. Exposures of outward-tilted Lewisian gneisses and lowermost (locally folded) Torridonian sandstones are examined in Forgotten and Sandy corries. These Archaean and Proterozoic basement rocks are unconformably capped by Paleocene breccias and ignimbrites of the Rum caldera infill succession, a relationship that records a phenomenal pre-caldera uplift of >1km. Also examined is the three-dimensional relationship between the intrusive rhyodacite facies and the extrusive facies. Historically important exposures that record the wholesale remelting of earlier felsic rocks by the later ultrabasic magmas are seen just east of Ainshval. Other exposures that record evidence of localised hybridisation between the remobilised felsic and invading ultrabasic melts are also seen. Spectacular views may be savoured from Bealach an Fhuarain, the Ainshval ridge, and Sgurr nan Gillean peak.

This (Figure 62) route comprises a series of steep and physically challenging hikes; the maximum elevation climbed to is 760 m, though the total height climbed is around 950 m. In some places, one passes along narrow ridges or ledges that are very close to cliffs over 100 m in height. It is therefore highly inadvisable to attempt much of this route in poor weather or visibility. There are superb views from the summits and from upper Glen Dibidil. Ten to twelve hours are required to complete the route, which, given its length and arduous nature, should be started from and ended at the Dibidil bothy.

Locality 8.1 [NM 3899 9294]

Lower east side of Sgurr nan Gillean – contact between intrusive breccia and mesobreccia

From the Dibidil bothy, walk north-west past the north-east side of the uhuilingu (otone walled sheep pens), and find the path to Papadil. Oblique to the path is a low north-west-trending grassy ridge. Proceed uphill along the top of this ridge toward the mouth of Nameless Corrie, the large corrie just north of Sgurr nan Gillean (the 'Stony Corrie' of Hughes, 1960a), until pinkish outcrops of 'Am Màm-type' intrusive breccia are reached (cf. Excursion 2, on the east side of Loch Gainmhich). Here, metre-scale blocks of gabbro, dolerite, Torridonian sandstone and Lewisian gneiss are enveloped in the creamy, coarse, 'tuffaceous' matrix that also contains numerous lobate fine-grained mafic inclusions of 1–6 cm diameter. Just upslope of the intrusive breccia outcrop are more rugged-looking red crags of feldspathic-sandstone-dominated mesobreccia. The north-east-trending contact between these rock types is directly observable at one point only [NM 38993 92940]. In this small exposure, at about 135 m OD on the south-west side of a small north-west-trending gully, relatively fine and somewhat crushed-looking mesobreccia overlies the intrusive breccia along a sharp contact that dips at about 50° to the north-west. The contact is marked on the intrusive breccia side by a 1–2 cm-thick dark grey zone with a fine-grained matrix and scattered feldspar phenocrysts. Intrusive breccia adjacent to this dark zone contains mafic inclusions aligned parallel to the contact. Moreover, the intrusive breccia matrix and the dark outer zone are undeformed. The intrusive breccia therefore post-dates the overlying mesobreccia and any faulting that might have affected the mesobreccia hereabouts, and controlled the intrusive breccia emplacement. On the north-west side of the gully, the mesobreccia–intrusive breccia boundary is offset a few metres downslope along a small fault that runs through the gully. The gully can be traced downslope from here past the sheilings as far as the mouth of the Dibidil River. As the fault surface is not visible, dextral strike-slip and/or normal fault motion (north-east side downthrown) could have generated the observed offset of the boundary. The 120° trend of the fault is typical of the 120–140° range for the many fractures and minor faults that cut through most of the rock units around the eastern and southern sectors of Sgurr nan Gillean. Such a fault pattern could have been generated by local doming (e.g. caused by the later mafic intrusions), or by the regional north-east to south-west extensional regime during the Palaeogene (cf. England, 1988).

Locality 8.2 [NM 3876 9293]

Lower east side of Sgurr nan Gillean – enigmatic Torridonian rocks above rhyodacite (extrusive?) and mesobreccia

Walk due west uphill from Locality 8.1, past more exposures of meso-breccia and some north-east-trending exposures of rhyodacite. About 250 m west of the intrusive breccia–mesobreccia contact, mudstones and siltstones are encountered, for example at [NM 38760 92925]. Note that although locally folded and brecciated (e.g. at [NM 38735 92970]), bedding usually strikes 050–080 and dips at 50–80° to the north-west. Farther north, the slope steepens to form the cliffs in the southern wall of Nameless Corrie, so follow the contour and aim to walk below or along the base of these cliffs. Note that the Torridonian rocks change northwards from thin, silty, and dark grey beds (TCDL) to thicker, sandier, and pink-coloured beds (TCAM; e.g. at [NM 38630 93150]), but that bedding strike remains similar to that farther south (albeit dip direction locally switches to south-east – Figure 62).

The exact explanation for the occurrence of this zone of coherent Torridonian beds at its present structural position is open to some debate. The internal structure commonly appears chaotic which, together with the volcanosedimentary successions (mesobreccia, tuffs, and ignimbrites) above and below it, has led to the suggestion that it is a landslide or debris avalanche deposit (megabreccia) related to caldera subsidence (Errington, in Emeleus, 1997). Alternatively, this zone of Torridonian rocks may represent a deformed but still fairly coherent part of the caldera floor, which has been faulted over the underlying volcanosedimentary succession during some form of later resurgence.

Locality 8.3 [NM 3828 9346]

Nameless Corrie – an ignimbrite vent system

From the base of the cliffs in the south-east wall of Nameless Corrie, contour north-west around and into the corrie until a contact between coherent Torridonian rocks and rhyodacite is found near a sharp bend in the corrie stream ([NM 38275 93460]; Locality 8.3a). Note on the way that bedding in the pinkish sandstones swings to a consistent north-north-west strike with a moderate east or north-east dip. On the south-west side of the stream, different facies of rhyodacite are visible inside a basaltic margin that chills very sharply against sandstone (Figure 66). The other contact of the 10–35 cm-thick basaltic zone is unchilled and locally quite undulose against a massive, white-weathering rhyodacite that contains several lobate mafic inclusions, and has rare narrow protrusions into the basaltic zone. These features show a liquid-liquid relationship between the basalt and rhyodacite, both of which were emplaced within a very close space of time to form a composite intrusion. About a metre north from the basalt–sandstone contact is a sharp transition from white-weathering rhyodacite to a darker and smoother weathering rhyodacite (also mafic inclusion-bearing – Figure 66). Just a few metres farther north of this latter transition, the dark rhyodacite displays a steep fiamme-like foliation that generally dips parallel to the outer basalt–sandstone contact. Around 150 m upslope to the west [NM 38148 93442] (Locality 8.3b) and about 10 m north of the contact with the Torridonian, another zone of the 'white-weathering', mafic inclusion-bearing rhyodacite facies occurs in sharp contact with, but north of, the dark, strongly-foliated rhyodacite facies. There thus seems to have been multiple emplacement episodes of the different facies in this intrusive rhyodacite body.

At [NM 38285 93712] (Locality 8.3c), a 50–90 cm-wide linear zone of breccia runs diagonally across a vertical rhyodacite face. The breccia is composed of sandstone and rhyodacite clasts of up to 8 cm diameter in a

117

rhyodacite matrix, and displays a somewhat diffuse and slightly irregular contact to the host rhyodacite. This breccia zone is very similar to many other 'linear' breccia zones found within the rhyodacite of Nameless Corrie; such zones are usually concordant with the steep to vertical rhyodacite foliation, and some are graded (e.g. at [NM 3886 9338]). Both breccia zones and fiamme foliation are sharply folded in some places; abrupt swings of up to 90° are seen in their strike directions, as at [NM 38459 93625]. At many points away from the liquid-liquid outer contact, e.g. [NM 38285 93712], the rhyodacite fiamme are chunky or lumpy in shape (very low width/length aspect ratios). Together with the concordant and locally graded breccia zones, such rhyodacite, of which there is much within the central part of Nameless Corrie, is thus lithologically more akin to moderately welded ignimbrite. This combination of an intrusive marginal facies and a more-fragmental, possibly extrusive interior facies, both of which dip steeply and discordantly to surrounding rocks (cf. Localities 8.5 and 8.9), may represent a feeder and eruptive vent system (Figure 67 – cf. intrusive rhyodacites of the Northern Marginal Zone [Emeleus, 1997]).

A short distance north-east of the 'linear' breccia zone, metre-size patches of mesobreccia (lacking a rhyodacite component, e.g. at [NM 38460 93556]) appear wholly enclosed in rhyodacite, and are possibly large xenoliths. Around 60 m east of the 'linear' breccia zone and 60 m north of the corrie stream, the composite intrusive outer rhyodacite contact is again found adjacent to mesobreccia and Torridonian rocks. At this location [NM 38455 93551] (Locality 8.3d), an undeformed basaltic marginal zone to the rhyodacite truncates and very sharply chills against

Opposite page: Figure 66.
Intrusive rhyodacite contacts and internal facies variations, Nameless Corrie, Dibidil.
a. Schematic sketch of facies variations within the intrusive rhyodacite as one moves away from the southern contact.
b. Photo of contacts in (a).
c. Close up of mafic inclusions in the 'light' rhyodacite facies. Many inclusions are angular, which may reflect reworking of conduit lining, and some inclusions contain blocky 'rhyodacite' plagioclase crystals.
d. Contact between light and dark rhyodacite facies, which is locally streaky with schlieren of dark rhyodacite in light rhyodacite.

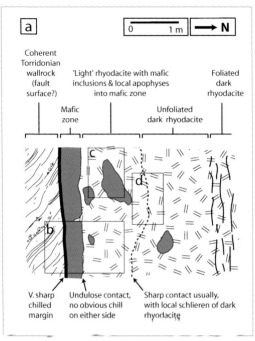

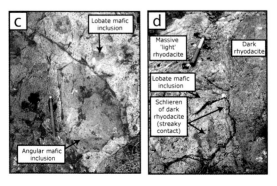

119

tightly folded and hornfelsed siltstone (TCDL), proving that rhyodacite intrusion here post-dates the folding of the Torridonian. The fold (antiform) in TCDL plunges steeply west and its hinge zone is brecciated. Other evidence of folding in the Torridonian rocks is found a few tens of metres to the south-east, where a series of S-folds is seen in steeply dipping, heavily crushed and brecciated, baked siltstone (TCDL). On the way down to this point, note that the Torridonian rocks generally maintain a north-north-west strike and dip east, but gradually fine downslope to comprise laminated siltstones and mudstones (TCDL). The somewhat enigmatic area of Torridonian rocks on the northern flank of Sgurr nan Gillean and the south side of Nameless Corrie thus comprises a largely undisrupted succession (TCAM–TCDL) that is apparently overturned, being inclined to the east, but younging to the west (Figure 62).

Notice also that the rocks of Nameless Corrie, in common with most of the pre-gabbro rocks exposed in Glen Dibidil, are cut by numerous basaltic dykes and inclined sheets, which are conspicuous on the glacially scoured rhyodacite slabs.

Figure 67. Schematic sketch showing the relationship of the ignimbrite feeder system to the caldera infill. (Adapted from Freundt et al., 2000.)

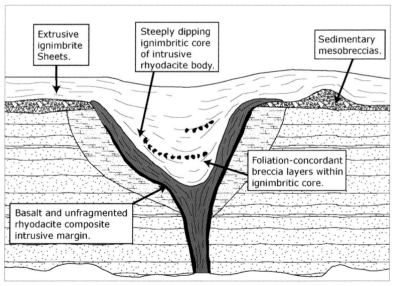

Locality 8.4 [NM 3863 9349]

Nameless Corrie – a hybrid contact rock ('needle-rock')

About 200 m east and north-east of Locality 8.3, a large area of pinkish-weathering hybrid rocks (locally granodioritic) is exposed on slabs and in low crags north of the stream running from Nameless Corrie, and in a knoll on the southern side (Figures 62, 63). The sharp contact between rhyodacite and hybrid rock is exposed along the corrie stream at about [NM 38625 93490] (c. 210 m OD). These hybrids are characterised by acicular amphibole (and orthopyroxene) and plagioclase. They are marginal to the gabbro of lower Glen Dibidil, with which they are found to be in sharp contact north of the stream (e.g. [NM 3902 9368]). The gabbro is the later intrusion. On emplacement, it reacted with rhyodacite to produce a hybridised, intermediate rock of the type commonly found elsewhere on Rum at contacts between gabbros and felsic rocks (Greenwood, 1987).

Locality 8.5 [NM 3851 9427]

Forgotten Corrie – tilted Torridonian basement, bedded mesobreccia, and extrusive vs. intrusive rhyodacite

From Locality 8.4 contour northwards along the rim of Nameless Corrie and skirt around the steep eastern flank of the ridge between Nameless and Forgotten corries at about 250 m OD. Climb up toward the mouth of Forgotten Corrie and pass typically south-east- to east-inclined Torridonian beds (TCDF and TCDL), until the stream flowing from the corrie is reached at about 350 m OD. Several tens of metres to the north-west, mesobreccia dominated by gritty sandstone (TCDF) clasts is exposed in crags that overlook the grassy slope down to the Dibidil River. At Locality 8.5 [NM 38505 94266], a few metres north of a contact with north-west-dipping sandstone, the mesobreccia contains a north-west-dipping (40–50°) lens of lithic tuff with rare accretionary lapilli. Around 150 m to the north-north-west are similarly north-west-dipping contacts between mesobreccia, a clast-aligned lithic tuff, and unchilled, fiamme-rich rhyodacite [NM 38485 94327]. The fiamme define a contact-parallel foliation, and become gradually less abundant about a metre above the basal contact. Two foliation-

121

concordant and normally graded lithic tuff layers (or lenses), with sharp bases but diffuse tops to enclosing rhyodacite, are also visible here, a metre or two above the basal contact (similar to the south-west end of Meall Breac – Excursion 2).

In the steep north wall of the corrie, about 80 m to the south-west, there is a prominent, 15 m-wide, subvertical cleft occupied by a brown-weathering dyke. Along the foot of the corrie wall and a few metres north-east of this dyke is a small exposure of rhyodacite with a thin sub-vertical lithic trail that passes up through undisturbed north-west-dipping fiamme. This feature strongly resembles a lithic lapilli degassing pipe ('fossil fumarole') characteristic of high-temperature ignimbrites. The graded lithic tuff lenses, the basal contact relationship to underlying bedded mesobreccia, and the lithic trail are strong evidence for an extrusive origin of the rhyodacite at this location.

In contrast, rhyodacite forming the cliffs of the corrie wall has a strong foliation that dips steeply (60–75°) to the east-south-east. This foliation can be tracked along strike for c. 150 m to the south-west and across the stream, where the rhyodacite displays a strongly chilled, south-east-dipping contact against mesobreccia [NM 3832 9420]. Hereabouts, vertical 'fluidised-looking' zones occur in the mesobreccia just above the contact (Figure 68). These structures are possibly generated by gas flow from intruding rhyodacite through poorly consolidated mesobreccia. In plan view, this intrusive rhyodacite body truncates the bedded mesobreccias and north-west-dipping extrusive rhyodacites that crop out to the north-east. Along strike to the south-west, the light-grey intrusive rhyodacite is sharply chilled against the dark-grey Torridonian sandstone in the southern wall of Forgotten Corrie, and this east-south-east-dipping contact continues through Nameless Corrie to Sgurr nan Gillean (Figures 62, 63).

Locality 8.6 [NM 3821 9453]

Upper Glen Dibidil – Hughes' back-veining contact between the ultrabasic and felsic rocks (rhyodacites)

This locality is a classic in the history of geological investigations on Rum. Walk north-east out of Forgotten Corrie and, while maintaining as much altitude as possible, contour north-west (at c. 330 m OD), between the

Figure 68. Subvertical foliated fluidised-looking zone (gas escape/hydromagmatic) in mesobreccia, next to sharp south-dipping contact with intrusive rhyodacite. Locality 8.5, Forgotten Corrie. Scale: hammer shaft c. 35 cm.

Figure 69. Backveined margins of the Eastern Layered Intrusion, north-east slopes of Ainshval (Locality 8.6). Remobilised felsic material (white), derived from adjoining rhyodacite, encloses blocks of brown-weathering peridotite and other mafic lithologies. The ultra-basic layers of Trollaval loom in the background right. Upper Glen Dibidil, near Bealac an Fhuarain. Scale: hammer shaft c. 35 cm.

steep, lowermost crags on Ainshval and the tops of the grassy slopes down to the Dibidil River. The break of slope approximately delineates the boundary between easily weathered peridotite and gabbro of the Eastern Layered Intrusion and tough, thermally altered rhyodacite, mesobreccia and Torridonian rocks. After some 300–400 m, at c. [NM 3821 9453], the slabs expose a breccia consisting of angular to sub-angular blocks of yellow-brown-weathering peridotite and other mafic lithologies in a finely crystalline, felsic matrix (Figure 69). Early geologists working on Rum interpreted this as evidence that the adjacent rhyodacite (and other felsic rocks) intruded, and therefore post-dated, the gabbros and peridotites of the Layered Centre (e.g. Harker, 1908). However, Hughes (1960a) subsequently demonstrated that melting and mobilisation (rheomorphism) of earlier silicic rocks, of relatively low melting point, by later intensely hot peridotite and gabbro intrusions could generate a 'backveining' felsic matrix that locally enclosed chunks of the peridotite and gabbro. Similar backveining contacts were subsequently recognised elsewhere on the island (e.g. Meall Breac, Cnapan Breaca, Excursion 2; Dunham, 1964).

123

Locality 8.7 [NM 3790 9487]

Bealach an Fhuarain – views of Glen Dibidil, Trollaval, Fiachanis
and Harris

Continue north-west to Bealach an Fhuarain (c. 515 m OD; [NM 3790 9487]), the col between Ainshval and Trollaval. From here, there are good views south, down the length of the glacial Glen Dibidil, and east across the valley to the layered rocks of Askival. To the north, the layering of peridotite and gabbro is prominent in the south-facing cliffs of Trollaval. To the west through the col is a fine view over Fiachanis, Loch Fiachanis, and Harris. On a clear day the lighthouse on the pitchstone reef of Oigh-sgeir (the reef is probably a continuation of the Sgurr of Eigg pitchstone flow) and some of the Outer Hebridean islands are visible on the horizon.

OPTIONS:
From the head of Glen Dibidil there is the option to return to the Dibidil Bothy or to Kinloch Castle. Return to Kinloch can be made either via Glen Dibidil and the Dibidil path, or through Bealach an Oir [NM 386 953], around the head of Atlantic corrie to Bealach Bairc-mheall [NM 3866 9705], and down Coire Dubh (this option should not be selected if the weather is in any way bad). The journey time for either route is around 3–3½ hours (perhaps shorter for the second option).

With the second option, contour north-east from Bealach an Oir at about 450 m OD for c. 800 m across the steep, grassy and scree-covered slopes on the north-west side of Askival. Extreme care must be exercised, since some of the scree is unstable and some partly obscured by vegetation. Then climb to nearly 550 m OD to a point about 150 m west-north-west of the col between Askival and Hallival (i.e. to c. [NM 3920 9600]). Continue north on a broad shelf for c. 500 m, keeping at 550 m OD, then walk north-north-west and north-west down gentle slopes to Bealach Bairc-mheall and the head of Coire Dubh. From here, it is an easy descent to the corrie floor and down to Kinloch.

For those continuing the excursion route from Bealach an Fhuarain, the last three localities on this route provide further insights into the volcano-tectonic evolution of the Southern Mountains (and great views), but should only be visited in good weather and with sufficient daylight remaining. The night would normally be spent at the Dibidil bothy.

Locality 8.8 [NM 3743 9404]

Sandy Corrie – a rare caldera floor through volcanosedimentary infill succession

From Bealach an Fhuarain, walk westward for about 500 m down into the valley above Fiachanis, past exposures of gabbro. Once safely below the steep cliffs on the north-west flank of Ainshval (at c.[NM 373 948]), continue in a south-west direction, contouring at about 350–400 m OD around to the base of the cliffs on the south-west side of the mountain and into Sandy Corrie. On the way, note the change from gabbro to Lewisian gneiss. Climb towards the south-facing cliffs of the north wall of the corrie. In and around these cliffs, at about 500 m OD, is the basal unconformity between the Torridonian rocks and underlying gneiss, e.g. [NM 3743 9404]. A classic basal conglomerate of gneiss cobbles and boulders is overlain by very coarse, gritty, and often cross-bedded sandstones (TCDF), which dip at about 40–50° to the east. Conformably overlying the TCDF beds and a zone of transitional facies (Nicholson, 1992), are laminated siltstones and mudstones of the Laimhrig Shale Member [NM 37505, 94083]. Note that relative to the gentle and regional north-west dip of the succession outside the Main Ring Fault, the Torridonian rocks and gneisses exposed in Sandy Corrie have been outwardly tilted and uplifted by at least 1.5 km.

The basement TCDL rocks are frequently brecciated farther upslope, but the breccia is usually clast supported and most clasts remain orientated parallel to the bedding seen below. These brecciated rocks are sharply overlain by a reverse-graded and strongly clast-aligned sandstone at [NM 37637 94009]. This sandstone contains clasts of sandstone and siltstone, accretionary lapilli and blocky plagioclase crystals, and it grades up into rhyodacite with abundant fine fiamme and shards. Just upslope, across a small gap in exposure, are more exposures of rhyodacite; at the base of one of these is a zone of lithic tuff with gradational contacts to the overlying rhyodacite. This 20 m-thick rhyodacite body is sheet-like in form; its contacts and the fiamme within it dip at 20–35° to the east-south-east. The fiamme comprise light- and dark-weathering types, with a zoned distribution (dark types are concentrated toward the base). Towards the top of the sheet some fiamme are up to 1 m long and 15 cm thick. A generally matrix-supported mesobreccia of predominantly sandstone clasts (TCDF?) overlies

125

this rhyodacite sheet, and is markedly different to the brecciated TCDL below. Above the 30 m-thick mesobreccia is green sandstone, which is in sharp contact with more rhyodacite upslope. The fiamme in this upper rhyodacite sheet are orientated parallel to those in the lower sheet and persist until the top of the ridge.

The north wall of Sandy Corrie thus contains uplifted and tilted rocks of the lower parts of the regional stratigraphical succession (caldera floor), upon which lie sedimentary and pyroclastic rocks (caldera infill). Like at Beinn nan Stac, there seem to be two (possibly correlatable) ignimbrites preserved (Figure 70). The sequence seen on the northern side of Sandy Corrie occurs on the southern side also, where it is picked out by featuring. Caldera floor through infill successions, as seen in such a relatively undisturbed state on Rum, are rarely found in the geological record.

Locality 8.9 [NM 3783 9330]

Headwall of Nameless Corrie – intrusive rhyodacite meets the extrusive rhyodacite sheet of Sgurr nan Gillean peak

Climb south-east up from Sandy Corrie to the col in the ridge above [NM 3780 9384]. Walk southward along the ridge to the south side of the mid-ridge peak, Sgurr nan Goibhrean (754 m OD on OS map; Goat Mountain on Hughes' 1960a map) from which extends the spur to Leac a'Chaisteil. From here, at [NM 37760 93330], an inclined ledge runs south-east down into Nameless Corrie. Less than 100 m from the ridge and along this ledge, at [NM 37831 93297], is the base of the large sheet-like mass of rhyodacite that caps Sgurr nan Gillean. The sheet rests on a thin veneer of mesobreccia (gneiss and feldspathic sandstone clasts) that overlies east-inclined pinkish sandstones (TCAM). The lower metre or so of the rhyodacite sheet displays alternating layers of fine tuff and crystal tuffs with wavy and planar bedding structures – probably surge deposits. Above these bedded tuffs is a gradational contact to fiamme-rich rhyodacite, the foliation in which is concordant to the layered tuffs below.

About 35 m north-west and along its strike, the base contact abruptly disappears into more-or-less massive rhyodacite. The intrusive margin of the Nameless Corrie rhyodacite mass is traceable from Locality 8.3 to just a few metres below this point (Figures 62, 63). Thus, although its

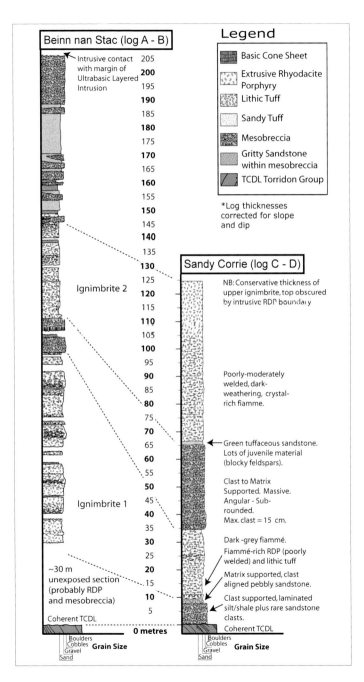

Beinn nan Stac (log A - B)

Intrusive contact with margin of Ultrabasic Layered Intrusion — 205, 200, 195, 190

Ignimbrite 2

Ignimbrite 1

~30 m unexposed section (probably RDP and mesobreccia)

Coherent TCDL

Boulders / Cobbles / Gravel / Sand — **Grain Size**

0 metres

Legend

▓ Basic Cone Sheet

▒ Extrusive Rhyodacite Porphyry

░ Lithic Tuff

□ Sandy Tuff

▓ Mesobreccia

▒ Gritty Sandstone within mesobreccia

▨ TCDL Torridon Group

*Log thicknesses corrected for slope and dip

Sandy Corrie (log C - D)

NB: Conservative thickness of upper ignimbrite, top obscured by intrusive RDP boundary

Poorly-moderately welded, dark-weathering, crystal-rich fiamme.

Green tuffaceous sandstone. Lots of juvenile material (blocky feldspars).

Clast to Matrix Supported. Massive. Angular - Sub-rounded. Max. clast = 15 cm.

Dark -grey fiammé. Fiammé-rich RDP (poorly welded) and lithic tuff

Matrix supported, clast aligned pebbly sandstone.

Clast supported, laminated silt/shale plus rare sandstone clasts.

Coherent TCDL

Boulders / Cobbles / Gravel / Sand — **Grain Size**

Figure 70.
Schematic log of caldera-fill ignimbrite successions on Beinn nan Stac and in Sandy Corrie (see Figure 62 for log lines).

127

characteristic basaltic margin disappears here, the steeply-foliated intrusive rhyodacite apparently truncates the extrusive rhyodacite sheet (or at least its base). This relationship may be explained by initial intrusion into the pre-caldera basement of a composite basalt–rhyodacite body (dyke), which subsequently fragmented and erupted once near the surface. This eruption feeder system may have supplied the material deposited as the ignimbrite sheet that caps Sgurr nan Gillean; if a solidified ignimbrite sheet existed prior to composite intrusion, one might expect to see a basaltic margin against its base. Continuous and/or subsequent through flow and eruptions of rhyodacite (cf. Localities 7.2, 7.3, 7.8) could then have produced the apparently discordant relationship between the lower parts of the caldera fill and the vent system (Figure 67).

Syn-eruptive faulting may also complicate these field relationships. The similarly inclined TCDF/TCDL boundaries east of Forgotten Corrie and on the other side of the ridge in Sandy Corrie are vertically offset by 600–1000 m. Though perhaps also related to folding of the basement, this apparent discontinuity may be due to a fault between the corries. A candidate fault surface is the sharp, east- to south-east-inclined surface of the intrusive rhyodacite margin seen earlier in Nameless and Forgotten corries (visible in the corrie wall opposite – Figures 62, 63). If so, this fault downthrows to the west, has a reverse sense of displacement, and is orientated concentric with the Main Ring Fault system. Such reverse ring faults, though rarely seen in the field, have long been invoked to solve the 'room problem' of caldera subsidence (cf. Anderson, 1936), and have been regarded as potential conduits for syn-caldera magma transport and eruption.

Locality 8.10 [NM 3802 9303]

Peak of Sgurr nan Gillean – views of the Hebrides and Western Scottish Highlands

On a clear day, Sgurr nan Gillean provides a superb 360° panorama across Rum, the Inner and Outer Hebrides, and the Western Scottish Highlands. Winding northward to Ainshval is the steep stony ridge, formed as glaciers carved out deep corries. Just behind Ainshval and to the north-east are the terraces of Trollaval, Askival and Hallival. The serrated peaks of the Skye Cuillin loom in the distance beyond Rum's north shore. At the time of emplacement, basic and ultrabasic layers stretched across the north-east flank of Glen Dibidil to meet their arched roof at Beinn nan Stac, which is composed of intensely-deformed country rocks and violently emplaced ignimbrites and breccias. The geologically ancient Western Highlands form the jagged horizon that extends north-east to south-east. Just south-east of Rum lie the lavas of Eigg and Muck, and beyond these to the south-south-east are the remnant Palaeogene central volcanoes of Ardnamurchan and Mull. The isles of Coll and Tiree, composed of Archaean Lewisian gneisses, appear to the south-west. To the west and north-west, the Outer Hebridean isles of Barra and South Uist hug the horizon across the Sea of the Hebrides, the waves of which crash into the high cliffs of Rum's Western Granite, just beyond Harris.

Descend from Sgurr nan Gillean westward down the scree slopes. After about a kilometre, you should have rounded the steep cliffs in Sgurr nan Gillean's south-west flank. There are then two options to return to Dibidil.

OPTIONS:

1. Shorter, but slightly trickier. Contour south east around the base of the steep cliffs and above the grassy slopes that overlook Papadil. After about 1.5 km, you should reach a small plateau at around 460 m elevation on the south side of Sgurr nan Gillean [NM 38000 92450]. From the plateau, it is fairly straightforward to drop into the corrie in the south side of Sgurr nan Gillean, and then you can pick your way down the grassy slopes for another kilometre eastward until the Papadil path is reached just above the Dibidil bothy.

2. Longer, but slightly easier. Drop down to Papadil (follow the streams), and then take the path back to Dibidil. This route is just less than 5 km in length, but is better marked and has a gentler descent to Dibidil.

Excursion 9

Lower Glen Dibidil – shoulder of Sgurr nan Gillean – Papadil

HIGHLIGHTS

This excursion highlights the complexity of the Main Ring Fault system between Dibidil and Papadil (Figures 62, 72), and the effects of the intrusion of the Layered Centre on the Torridonian country rocks. Evidence of antithetic motions on inner and outer strands of the Ring Fault system are seen, and a sedimentary origin for the 'mesobreccias' is demonstrated south of Sgurr nan Gillean. Also verified hereabouts is the close temporal and spatial relationship between intrusive rhyodacite and an enigmatic (Am Màm-type) intrusive breccia, as well as the later emplacement date of these rock types relative to the sedimentary mesobreccias. The Papadil Microgranite, thought to be the final instalment of Stage 1, is examined on the south-west slopes of Sgurr nan Gillean. The southernmost end of the influential Long Loch Fault is seen at Inbhir Ghill. Around Loch Papadil, ductile deformation and remobilisation of the Torridonian rocks by the Layered Centre is seen in spectacular contact exposures. Finally, unusual minor intrusions into the gently inclined uppermost member of the Torridonian succession of Rum are inspected.

This excursion will take a full day and it is best to start and finish from a base at or near the Dibidil bothy, in which case the total distance is about 7 km. Extremely fit persons could walk from Kinloch to Dibidil by the well-marked path, follow the excursion route and return to Kinloch by the same path. The total distance for this strenuous day would be about 23 km.

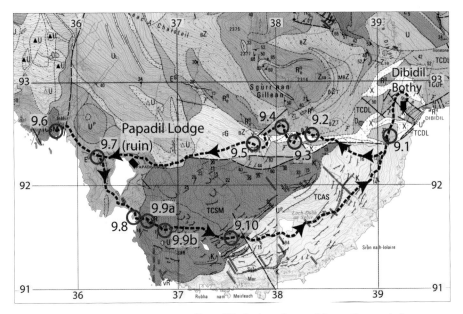

Figure 71. Geological map of the southern end of Rum from Sgurr nan Gillean to Rubha nam Meirleach. Excursion 9. (See pp. 148-49 for full key; based on SNH 1:20,000 solid geology map; © SNH.)

Locality 9.1 [NM 3916 9263]

Along the Papadil path – evidence for multiple movements on the Main Ring Fault

From the Dibidil bothy or ford, walk along the path toward Papadil. About 170 m west-south-west of the bothy at [NM 39138 92736], a few metres above the path, there are small, scattered exposures of feldspathic sandstone (TCAM). Bedding consistently strikes north-east and dips very steeply north-west. For a few hundred metres further upslope there are several exposures of laminated siltstone (TCDL), which strike north-east and dip north-west, but also young south-west (e.g. cross-laminations at [NM 38856 92642]). An overturned (outward-rotated) block of sandstone and siltstone (TCDL-TCAM) occupies the grassy slopes from just above the bothy to the steep crags on the lower slope of Sgurr nan Gillean (Figure 71). About 200 m south-west of the bothy, the path crosses a waterfall that cuts into gneiss [NM 3916 9263]. The overturned Torridonian beds just to

131

the north must have subsided along a fault to now lie inside this gneiss. This fault, the 'Southern Mountains Ring Fracture' of Hughes (1960a), is likely to be equivalent to the central strand of the Main Ring Fault system at Beinn nan Stac (Localities 7.3 and 7.4).

Just past a second waterfall cutting into gneiss [NM 3912 9248], about 220 m farther south on the path, are exposures of crushed-looking dark-grey siltstone (TCDL). These beds dip steeply north-west, as do feldspathic sandstones in an exposure 50 m farther south along the path. Another 150 m south along the path, thick-bedded, orange-pink, coarse feldspathic sandstones (TCAS) exhibit the shallow regional north-west dip. These beds form a thick succession that dominates much of the southern tip of Rum and, as in the north of the island, impart a characteristic terraced topography. The TCDL siltstone is probably a fault-bound sliver between TCAS sandstone and the Lewisian gneiss; the latter was uplifted along an outer strand of the Main Ring Fault system (Figure 72).

Locality 9.2 [NM 3845 9248]

Southern lower slope of Sgurr nan Gillean – depositional contact between mesobreccia and uplifted gneiss

Walk 350 m north-west upslope over gently inclined beds of feldspathic sandstone (TCAS) to where the second stream crossed on the path first bends to flow eastward at ([NM 38735 92390] – *c.* 240 m OD). The Outer Main Ring Fault continues from the last locality to here, where crushed coarse feldspathic sandstone (TCAS?) crops out adjacent to crags of gneiss upstream (e.g. at [NM 38569 92379]). Continue walking north-west next to the stream for another 200 m, past exposures of crushed gneiss and Am Màm-type breccia, as far as the gneiss exposures in the south wall of Sgurr nan Gillean's south corrie at approximately ([NM 38450 92480] – *c.* 360 m OD). An unfaulted depositional contact between gneiss and mesobreccia with feldspathic sandstone and gneiss clasts is exposed hereabouts. This demonstrates that the Lewisian gneiss here inside the inner ring fault was at the palaeosurface prior to deposition of the mesobreccia, and was probably raised to that level during the initial uplift along the Main Ring Fault, before subsiding to its present position.

Mesobreccia, tuffs & sandstones

Highly deformed TCDL - TCAM

Mesobreccia

TCDL

TCAM

Gneiss

Rhyodacite ignimbrite

Gneiss

Inner Ring Fault

TCAS

TCDL (deformed)

Mesobreccia

Outer Ring Fault

Sandstone (TCDL/TCAM?)

Gneiss & Am Mam-type breccia

TCAS

Figure 72. Annotated, panoramic view of the southern side of Sgurr nan Gillean, as viewed from west of the Papadil path.

Right:
Figure 73. Foliated outer facies of Am Màm-type breccia intruding mesobreccia. South slopes of Sgurr nan Gillean (Locality 9.3). Scale: hammer shaft *c.* 35 cm.

Below:
Figure 74. Diagram of the relationship between intrusive Am Màm-type breccia with porphyritic rhyodacite margins, and gneiss-dominated mesobreccia. South side of Sgurr nan Gillean (Locality 9.3).

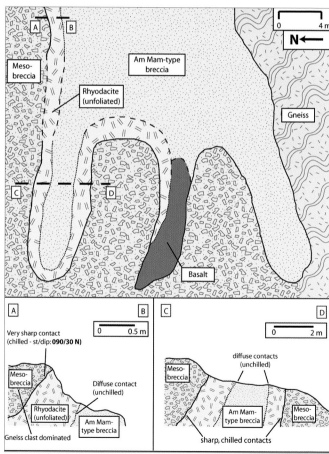

Locality 9.3 [NM 3826 9245]

Southern lower slope of Sgurr nan Gillean – contacts between mesobreccia, rhyodacite, and intrusive Am Màm-type breccia

Continue westward by the south wall of the corrie for another 150 m or so, and then walk south-east for another 50–60 m to where crags at about 420 m OD display a sharp north-west-dipping contact between light-grey and dark-red rocks [NM 38255, 92453]. The dark-red rock is sandstone-rich mesobreccia, which appears to be crushed near the contact (cf. Locality 8.1). The light-grey rock locally penetrates into, and encloses fragments of, the mesobreccia, and displays a strong foliation parallel to kinks in the contact (Figure 73). The foliated grey rock is a localised outer facies of the Am Màm-type breccia, more-typical exposures of which occur just a few metres south. Between the more-typical Am Màm-type breccia and the foliated outer facies are patches of rhyodacite-like material. A few metres west-south-west upslope [NM 38233 92439], rhyodacite occurs in sharp contact with the mesobreccia. In the adjacent exposure a metre or so south, rhyodacite is in a very intimate, intermingling contact with Am Màm-type breccia matrix. In an exposure 40 m further upslope [NM 38190 92423], rhyodacite is chilled sharply on one side against mesobreccia, but has a diffuse contact with Am Màm-type breccia matrix on the other. Rhyodacite (or similar material) thus seems locally to form a marginal facies to the Am Màm-type intrusive breccia, as is seen elsewhere (cf. Locality 7.9). Confirmation of this relationship is seen 130 m to the west on the plateau [NM 38074 92415], where rhyodacite and Am Màm-type breccia respectively form the margins and core of a composite dyke-like protrusion into mesobreccia; the rhyodacite is chilled only against mesobreccia (Figure 74). These relationships further demonstrate that the Am Màm-type breccia post-dates the lower parts of the caldera fill.

Locality 9.4 [NM 3810 9246]

Shoulder of Sgurr nan Gillean – alternating bedding in the mesobreccia

The mesobreccia of the Southern Mountains was long attributed to subterranean explosive fracturing of country rocks by gas from a cooling felsic

135

magma body at depth (Hughes, 1960a). Good evidence for a very different origin is seen at [NM 38101 92456], 40 m north-east of the composite rhyodacite and Am Màm-type breccia protrusion. Crude metre-scale bedding, defined by alternating feldspathic sandstone-rich (pink) and gneiss-rich (light-grey) zones, is visible in the mesobreccia, especially in late afternoon sunlight (Figure 75). The beds are lens shaped where defined in three dimensions (Figure 75); clasts are subangular to subrounded and generally coarse, with rare 2 m-diameter boulders. These exposures represent surficial deposits of interdigitating high-energy debris flows from discrete gneiss-rich and feldspathic sandstone-rich source areas. The bedding here and elsewhere around Sgurr nan Gillean dips generally toward the centre of the volcano, as seen in caldera-infill sequences elsewhere (Branney, 1995).

Locality 9.5 [NM 378 923]

Shoulder of Sgurr nan Gillean – the Papadil Microgranite

Exposures of light-grey microgranite that is lithologically and chemically very similar to the Western Granite occur about 250 m west-south-west of Locality 9.4 toward the top of the steep grassy slopes overlooking Papadil.

Figure 75. Bedded mesobreccia with alternating layers dominated by gneiss (cream coloured) and by feldspathic sandstone (pink coloured). South side of Sgurr nan Gillean. (Locality 9.4)

INSET: Close-up of a lens-shaped sandstone-dominated bed (above) and a gneiss-dominated bed (below).

Sandstone-rich bed | Gneiss-rich bed | Gneiss-rich bed
Sandstone-rich bed
Sandstone-rich bed

Small phenocrysts of feldspar are recognisable in a matrix of intergrown quartz and feldspar crystals. There are also abundant mafic minerals and numerous small, rounded, fine-grained mafic inclusions. Unlike the rhyodacite, quartz phenocrysts are rare or absent (Hughes, 1960a). The microgranite occupies most of the hollowed ground that slopes from Sgurr nan Gillean's steep south-west cliffs down to the Papadil Burn. Though its contacts are poorly exposed and understood, the Papadil Microgranite appears to truncate the mesobreccias, rhyodacite, and Am Màm-type breccias (Figure 71), and so probably post-dates these units. Apart from where crushed along the outer strand of the Main Ring Fault system, the microgranite is undeformed (Hughes, 1960a). Though Hughes thought otherwise, the Papadil Microgranite pre-dates the basic and ultrabasic rocks against which it is thermally metamorphosed, as does the Western Granite. Both microgranites are thus regarded as late Stage 1 intrusions.

Locality 9.6 [NM 3579 9247]

Sandstone melted by gabbro at Inbhir Gil

From Locality 9.5, descend gently westward for 2 km to Inbhir Gil [NM 3585 9260]. Along the way, note the change from microgranite to peridotite breccias and gabbro of the Central Intrusion on the slopes about 600 m north-east of Papadil Lodge. Nearby, it may be verified that peridotite comes to within a metre or so of baked sandstone (TCSM) in the Papadil Burn (at about [NM 3712 9225]), some 500 m east of the ruined lodge. The sandstone lies outside the Main Ring Fault which is evidently transgressed by the mafic rocks hereabouts. Traverse the low ground to the east side of the bay at Inbhir Ghil and cross the Allt na Gile. The steep-sided valley at Inbhir Ghil marks the course of the north–south Long Loch Fault. At Inbhir Ghil, leave the cove on its western side and trace the vertical contact between gabbro and Torridonian rocks as far south as possible (to c. [NM 3579 9247]). At low water, near the tidemark, this locality provides excellent exposures of partially melted Torridonian sandstone near the gabbro. Note the incipient break-up of dolerite 'xenoliths' in their silicic matrix. The gabbro is cut by thin (millimetre-scale), rheomorphic felsic veins and is chilled against the baked and partially melted sandstone.

Locality 9.7 [NM 3620 9228]

Peridotites around Loch Papadil

Return to the cove of Inbhir Ghil and leave by the south-eastern corner. Walk south-east for 300 m, then follow a wall east for about 250 m until an area of altered peridotite enclosed by gabbro is reached 200 m west of Loch Papadil [NM 3620 9228]. Follow the tongue of brown-weathering peridotite south for about 400 m and cross on to another brown-weathering peridotite area about 100 m west of Papadil Pinnacle [NM 3642 9183]. The contacts of this peridotite against gabbro are near vertical, as are those of the tongue to the north; both peridotite masses resemble rocks of the main ultrabasic mass north of Papadil. At Rubha na Pairce [NM 3615 9180], a small body of peridotite has intrusive wall and roof contacts against gabbro; the roof-like contact is nicely observed looking north from the peridotite. Note the extremely xenolithic character of the peridotite hereabouts, with as much as 80 per cent of the surface made up of rounded xenoliths of dolerite and gabbro, from 1 to 75 cm in diameter. The Rubha na Pairce peridotite is a much coarser grained rock than both the tongues seen earlier and Rum peridotites in general.

The gabbro hereabouts is unusual when compared with the normal Marginal Gabbro in that it is resistant to weathering. The gabbroic rocks in the shore sections are cut by abundant minor basic intrusions, the majority of which appear to be hornfelsed and to have developed large plates of biotite mica. The dykes commonly have 'welded' or annealed contacts with the host rocks.

Locality 9.8 [NM 3660 9173]

Melted sandstone around the bay south of Loch Papadil

Walk eastwards and cross the stream draining Loch Papadil. About 150 m east of Papadil Pinnacle, the gabbro on the coast is cut by an aplitic vein, probably of mobilised sedimentary material. Continue south-east along the coast to a point about 200 m east of Papadil Pinnacle. If the tide is high, it may not be possible to approach the locality from the west. In this case, it is easiest to detour northward around Loch Papadil, and to access the locality from a point on the Papadil path about 220 m south-south-east of Papadil Lodge.

Figure 76. Gabbro of the Central Intrusion (dark rock above figure) intruding bedded sandstone of the Sgorr Mhor Sandstone Member (TCSM), Aultbea Formation. Dark beds are relatively rich in heavy minerals. Note how the beds sag towards the zone of intrusion breccia along the contact. Coast south-east of Loch Papadil. (Locality 9.8)

INSET: Detail of the intrusion breccia zone at the gabbro–sandstone contact. The light-coloured felsic matrix has come from the partial melting of the sandstone. Scale: hammer shaft 30 cm

At Locality 9.8, gabbro occurs in near-vertical contact with sandstone (TCSM) in a low cliff at [NM 3660 9173]. Plastic deformation is very evident in the bedded sandstones which appear to sag towards the gabbro (Figure 76). Dolerite sheets have become fragmented in the relatively incompetent, partially melted sandstone, the fragments retaining their chilled edges. Note also the leucocratic sheet, of intermediate composition, exposed in the slopes below the cliff, which cuts both gabbro and sedimentary rocks.

Locality 9.9 [NM 3671 9164]

South-east of Papadil – minor intrusions and heavy-mineral bands in Torridonian sandstone

Climb eastwards across the contact seen at Locality 9.8. About 100 m south-east of the contact exposure, a thin pitchstone dyke crops out

139

(Locality 9.9a [NM 3671 9164]), and some 150 m farther to the south-east, south of the path (Locality 9.9b [NM 3681 9152]), there are exposures of sandstone with conspicuous dark layers rich in heavy minerals. These layers are characteristic of the highest member of the Torridon Group on Rum – the Sgorr Mhòr Member of the Aultbea Formation (TCSM) and are particularly well developed in coastal exposures near Rubha nam Meirleach [NM 368 911]. About 60 m to the south-east the sandstone is cut by a small peridotite plug. Continue east for about 350 m, to the north end of Loch nam Meirleach [NM 3729 9148]. About 150 m to the east, a 3 m-thick dolerite sill crops out (Locality 9.10 [NM 3740 9144]). This sheet is aphyric and typifies the group of conformable sills found in this southern tract. The sills usually have a vesicular band 5 cm below the upper contact; the vesicles are infilled with calcite, hydrogarnet, and other minerals. Follow the sill in a north-east direction until it is crossed by the path from Dibidil to Papadil at [NM 3863 9152]. A good view of the ridge from Ruinsival to Sgurr nan Gillean is obtained from the path. Contrast the vegetation and morphology of the gabbro at Papadil, the peridotite slopes to the north and the microgranite and rhyodacite to the north-east. Follow the path eastwards past the terraced features of the major bedding planes in feldspathic sandstone (TCAS) to the Dibidil bothy (Figure 62).

Figure 77. Evening view of eastern Rum from Laig Bay, Isle of Eigg.

References

ANDERSON, E. M. (1936): The dynamics of the formation of cone-sheets, ring-dykes and caldron-subsidences, *Proceedings of the Royal Society of Edinburgh*, **56**, pp. 128-63.

BAILEY, E. B. (1945): Tertiary igneous tectonics of Rhum, Inner Hebrides, *Quarterly Journal of the Geological Society, London*, **100**, pp. 165-91.

BAILEY, E. B. (1956): Hebridean notes: Rhum and Skye, *Liverpool and Manchester Geological Journal*, **1**, pp. 420-26.

BEDARD, J. H., SPARKS, R. S. J., RENNER, R., CHEADLE, M. J. and HALLWORTH, M. A. (1988): Peridotite sills and metasomatic gabbros in the Eastern Layered Series of the Rhum complex, *Journal of the Geological Society, London*, **145**, pp. 207-24.

BEDARD, J. H. and SPARKS, R. S. J. (1991): Comments on 'The Structure and Petrogenesis of the Trollaval and Ruinsival areas of the Rhum ultrabasic pluton' by A. Volker and B. G. J. Upton, *Transactions of the Royal Society of Edinburgh: Earth Sciences*, **82**, pp. 389-90.

BELL, B. R. and WILLIAMSON, I. T. (2002): Tertiary igneous activity, in TREWIN, N. H. (ed.): *The Geology of Scotland* (4th edition) (London: The Geological Society).

BINNS, P. E., McQUILLIN, R. and KENOLTY, K. (1974): The geology of the Sea of the Hebrides, *Report of the Institute of Geological Sciences*, no. **73/14**.

BLACK, G. P. (1952): The age relationship of the granophyre and basalt of Orval, Isle of Rhum, *Geological Magazine*, **91**, pp. 106-12.

BLACK, G. P. (1954): The acid rocks of Western Rhum, *Geological Magazine*, **91**, pp. 257-72.

BLAKE, D. H., ELWELL, R. W. D., GIBSON, I. L., SKELHORN, R. R. and WALKER, G. P. L. (1965): Some relationships resulting from the intimate association of acid and basic magmas, *Quarterly Journal of the Geological Society, London*, **121**, pp. 31-50.

BRANNEY, M. J. (1995): Downsag and extension of calderas: new perspectives on collapse geometries from ice melt, mining and volcanic subsidence, *Bulletin of Volcanology*, **57**, pp. 303-18.

BROWN, G. M. (1956): The layered ultrabasic rocks of Rhum, Inner Hebrides, *Philosophical Transactions of the Royal Society, London*, **240B**, pp. 1-53.

BUTCHER, A. R., YOUNG, I. M. and FAITHFUL, J. W. (1985): Finger structures in the Rhum Complex, *Geological Magazine*, **122**, pp. 491-502.

CHAMBERS, L. M., PRINGLE, M. S and PARRISH, R. R. (2005): Rapid formation of the Small Isles Tertiary centre constrained by precise 40Ar/39Ar and U-Pb ages, *Lithos*, **79**, pp. 367-84.

DAGLEY, P. and MUSSETT. A. E. (1981): Palaeomagnetism of the British Tertiary igneous province: Rhum and Canna, *Geophysical Journal of the Royal Astronomical Society*, **65**, pp. 475-91.

DONALDSON, C. H. (1974): Olivine crystal types in harrisitic rocks of the Rhum pluton and in Archean spinifex rocks, *Bulletin of the Geological Society of America*, **85**, pp. 1721-26.

DONALDSON, C. H. (1975): Ultrabasic breccias in layered intrusions. The Rhum Complex, *Journal of Geology*, **83**, pp. 33-45.

DONALDSON, C. H. (1976): An experimental investigation of olivine morphology, *Contributions to Mineralogy and Petrology*, **57**, pp. 187-213.

DONALDSON, C. H., DREVER, H. I. and JOHNSTON, R. (1973): Crystallisation of poikilo-macro-spherulitic feldspar in a Rhum peridotite, *Nature Physical Sciences*, **243**, pp. 69-70.

DONALDSON, C. H., TROLL, V. R. and EMELEUS, C. H. (2001): Felsites and breccias in the Northern Marginal Zone of the Rum Central Complex: changing views, *c.* 1900–2000, *Proceedings of the Yorkshire Geological Society*, **53**, pp. 167-75.

DUNHAM, A. C. (1964): A petrographic and geochemical study of back-veining and hybridization at a gabbro-felsite contact in Coire Dubh, Rhum, Invernesshire, *Mineralogical Magazine*, **33**, pp. 887-902.

DUNHAM, A. C. (1965): A new type of banding in ultrabasic rocks from Central Rhum, Invernesshire, Scotland, *American Mineralogist*, **50**, pp. 1410-20.

DUNHAM, A. C. (1968): The felsites, granophyre, explosion breccias and tuffisites of the north-eastern margin of the Tertiary igneous complex of Rhum, Invernesshire, *Quarterly Journal of the Geological Society, London*, **123**, pp. 327-52.

DUNHAM, A. C. and EMELEUS, C. H. (1967) The Tertiary geology of Rhum, Inner Hebrides, *Proceedings of the Geologists' Association*, **78**, pp. 391-418.

EMELEUS, C. H. (1973): Granophyre pebbles in Tertiary conglomerate on the Isle of Canna, Invernesshire, *Scottish Journal of Geology*, **9**, pp. 157-59.

EMELEUS, C. H. (1985): The Tertiary lavas and sediments of northwest Rhum, Inner Hebrides, *Geological Magazine*, **122**, 419-37.

EMELEUS, C. H. (1997): Geology of Rum and the adjacent islands, *Memoir of the British Geological Survey, Scotland*, Sheet 60.

EMELEUS, C. H. and BELL, B. R. (2005): *British regional geology: the Palaeogene volcanic districts of Scotland* (4th edition) (Nottingham: British Geological Survey).

EMELEUS, C. H., CHEADLE, M. J., HUNTER, R. H., UPTON, B. G. J. and WADSWORTH, W. J. (1996): The Rum Layered Suite, in CAWTHORN, R. G. (ed.): *Layered igneous rocks* (Amsterdam: Elsevier), pp. 403-40.

EMELEUS, C. H. and GYOPARI, M. C. (1992): British Tertiary Volcanic Province, *Geological Conservation Review Series* no. **4** (London: Chapman and Hall).

ENGLAND, R. W. (1988): The early Tertiary stress regime in NW Britain: evidence from the patterns of volcanic activity, in MORTON, A. C. and PARSON, L. M. (eds): *Early Tertiary volcanism and the opening of the NE Atlantic. Special Publication of the Geological Society of London*, **39**, pp. 381-89.

FAITHFULL, J. W. (1985): The Lower Eastern Layered Series of Rum, *Geological Magazine*, **122**, pp. 459-68.

FREUNDI, A., WILSON, C. J. N. and CAREY, S. N. (2000): Ignimbrites and block-and-ash flows, in SIGURDSSON, H., HOUGHTON, B., McNUTT, S., RYMER, H. and STIX, J. (eds): *Encyclopedia of Volcanoes* (San Diego: Academic Press), pp. 581-99.

FYFE, J. A., LONG, D. and EVANS, D. (1993): *United Kingdom offshore regional report: the geology of the Malin-Hebrides Sea area* (London: HMSO for the British Geological Survey).

GREENWOOD, R. C. (1985): *Geology and petrology of the margin of the Rhum Ultrabasic intrusion, Inner Hebridies, Scotland*, unpublished PhD Thesis, University of St Andrews.

GREENWOOD, R. C., DONALDSON, C. H. and EMELEUS, C. H. (1990): The contact zone of the Rhum ultrabasic intrusion: evidence of peridotite formation from magnesian magmas, *Journal of the Geological Society, London*, **147**, pp. 209-12.

HAMILTON, M. A., PEARSON, D. G., THOMPSON, R. N., KELLY, S. P. and EMELEUS, C. H. (1998): Rapid eruption of Skye lavas inferred from precise U-Pb and Ar-Ar dating of the Rum and Cuillin plutonic complexes, *Nature*, **394**, pp. 260-63.

HARKER, A. (1908): The geology of the Small Isles of Invernesshire, *Memoir of the Geological Survey, Scotland*, Sheet 60.

HOLNESS, M. B. (1999): Contact metamorphism and anatexis of Torridonian arkose by minor intrusions of the Rum Igneous Complex, Inner Hebrides, Scotland, *Geological Magazine*, **136**, pp. 527-42.

HOLNESS, M. B. (2002): Spherulitic textures formed during crystallization of partially melted arkose, Rum, Scotland, *Geological Magazine*, **139**, pp. 651-63.

HOLNESS, M. B. (2005): Spatial constraints on magma chamber replenishment events from textural observations of cumulates: the Rum Layered Intrusion, Scotland, *Journal of Petrology*, **46**, 1585-1601.

HOLNESS, M. B. (2007): Textural immaturity of cumulates as an indicator of magma chamber processes: infiltration and crystal accumulation in the Rum Eastern Layerd Intrusion, *Journal of the Geological Society, London*, **164**, pp. 529-39.

HOLNESS, M. B. and ISHERWOOD, C. E. (2003): The aureole of the Rum Tertiary Igneous Complex, Scotland, *Journal of the Geological Society, London*, **160**, pp. 15-27.

HOLNESS, M. B., CHEADLE, M. J. and MCKENZIE, D. (2005): The uses of changes in dihedral angle to decode late-stage textural evolution in cumulates, *Journal of Petrology*, **46**, pp. 1565-83.

HOLNESS, M. B., NIELSEN, T. F. D. and TEGNER, C. (2007a): Textural maturity of cumulates: a record of chamber filling, liquid assemblage, cooling rate and large-scale convection in mafic layered intrusions, *Journal of Petrology*, **48**, pp. 141-57.

HOLNESS, M. B., HALLWORTH, M. A., WOODS, A., SIDES, R. E. (2007b): Infiltration metasomatism of cumulates by intrusive magma replenishment: the Wavy Horizon, Isle of Rum, Scotland, *Journal of Petrology*, **48**, pp. 563-87.

HUDSON, J. and ALLWRIGHT, A. (2003): *The Geology of Eigg* (Isle of Eigg Heritage Trust).

HUGHES, C. J. (1960a): The Southern Mountains Igneous Complex, Isle of Rhum, *Quarterly Journal of the Geological Society, London*, **116**, pp. 111-38.

HUGHES, C. J. (1960b): An occurrence of tillyite-bearing limestone in the Isle of Rhum, Inner Hebrides, *Geological Magazine*, **97**, pp. 384-88.

HUGHES, C. J., WADSWORTH, W. J. and EMELEUS, C. H. (1957): The contact between Tertiary granophyre and Torridonian arkose on Minishal, Isle of Rhum, *Geological Magazine*, **94**, pp. 337-39.

JOLLEY, D. W. (1997): Palaeosurface palynofloras of the Skye lava field and the age of the British Tertiary volcanic province, in WIDDOWSON, M. (ed.): Palaeosurfaces: Recognition, Reconstruction and Palaeoenvironmental

Interpretation, *Geological Society, London, Special Publication*, **120**, pp. 67-94.

LEE, C. E. (1981): Post depositional structures in the Bushveld Complex mafic sequence, *Journal of the Geological Society of London*, **138**, pp. 327-41.

McCLURG, J. E. (1982): *Petrology and evolution of the northern part of the Rhum ultrabasic complex*, unpublished PhD thesis, University of Edinburgh.

NICHOLSON, P. G. (1992): Precambrian: Upper Proterozoic Torridon Group, in COPE, J. C. W., INGHAM, J. K. and RAWSON, P. F. (eds): Atlas of palaeogeography and lithofacies, *Memoir of the Geological Society of London*, no. **13**, pp. 5-7.

NICHOLSON, P. G. (1993): A basin reappraisal of the Proterozoic Torridon Group, Northwest Scotland, in FROSTICK, L. E. and STEEL, R. J. (eds): Tectonic Controls and Signatures in Sedimentary Successions, *International Association of Sedimentologists, Special Publications*, **20**, pp. 183-202.

O'DRISCOLL, B., DONALDSON, C. H., TROLL, V. R., JERRAM, D. A. and EMELEUS, C. H. (2007a): An origin for harrisitic and granular olivine in the Rum Layered Suite, NW Scotland: a crystal size distribution study, *Journal of Petrology*, **48**, pp. 253-70.

O'DRISCOLL, B., HARGRAVES, R. B., EMELEUS, C. H., TROLL, V. R., DONALDSON, C. H. and REAVY, R. J. (2007b): Magmatic lineations inferred from anisotropy of magnetic susceptibility fabrics in Units 8, 9, and 10 of the Rum Eastern Layered Series, NW Scotland, *Lithos*, **98**, pp. 27-44.

PALACZ, Z. A. and TAIT, S. R. (1985): Isotopes and geochemical investigation of unit 10 from the Eastern Layered Series of the Rhum Intrusion, Northwest Scotland, *Geological Magazine*, **122**, pp. 485-90.

PEARSON, D. G., EMELEUS, C. H. and KELLEY, S. P. (1996): Precise 40Ar/39Ar age for the initation of Palaeogene volcanism in the Inner Hebrides and its regional significance, *Journal of the Geological Society of London*, **153**, pp. 815-18.

POWER, M. R., PIRRIE, D., and ANDERSON, J. C. Ø. (2003): Diversity of platinum group element mineralization styles in the North Atlantic Igneous Province: new evidence from Rum, UK, *Geological Magazine*, **140**, pp. 499–512.

RENNER, R. and PALACZ, Z. A. (1987): Basaltic replenishment of the Rhum magma chamber: evidence from Unit 14, *Journal of the Geological Society, London*, **144**, pp. 961-70.

ROBBINS, B. (1982): Finger structures in the Lille Kufjord Layered Intrusion, Finnmark, Norway, *Contributions to Mineralogy and Petrology*, **81**, pp. 290-95.

SMITH, N. J. (1985): The age and structural setting of limestones and basalts on the Main Ring Fault in southeast Rhum, *Geological Magazine*, **122**, pp. 439-45.

STEEL, R. J. (1974): New Red Sandstone piedmont and floodplain sedimentation in the Hebridean Province, Scotland, *Journal of Sedimentary Petrology*, **44**, pp. 336-57.

STEEL, R. J. (1977): Triassic rift basins in NW Scotland, their configuration, infilling and development, in FINSTAD, K. C. and SELLEY, R. C. (eds): *Proceedings of the Northern North Sea Symposium* (Stavanger: Norwegian Petroleum Society), Paper 7.

TAIT, S. R. (1985): Fluid dynamic and geochemical evolution of cyclic unit 10, Rhum, Eastern Layered Series, *Geological Magazine*, **122**, pp. 469-84.

TILLEY, C. E. (1944): A note on the gneisses of Rhum, *Geological Magazine*, **81**, pp. 129-31.

TROLL, V. R., EMELEUS, C. H., and DONALDSON, C. H. (2000): Caldera formation in the Rum central igneous complex, Scotland, *Bulletin of Volcanology*, **62**, pp. 301-17.

TROLL, V. R., DONALDSON, C. H. and EMELEUS, C. H. (2004): Pre-eruptive magma mixing in ash-flow deposits in the Tertiary Rum Igneous Centre, Scotland, *Contributions to Mineralogy and Petrology*, **147**, pp. 722-39.

UPTON, B. G. J., SKOVGAARD, A. C., McCLURG, J. E., KIRSTEIN, L., CHEADLE, M. J., EMELEUS, C. H., WADSWORTH, W. J. and FALLICK, A. E. (2002): Picritic magmas and the Rum ultramafic complex, Scotland, *Geological Magazine*, **139**, pp. 437-52.

VOLKER, J. A. and UPTON, B. G. J. (1990): The structure and petrogenesis of the Trallval and Ruinsival areas of the Rhum ultrabasic pluton, *Transactions of the Royal Society of Edinburgh: Earth Sciences*, **81**, pp. 69-88.

VOLKER, J. A. and UPTON, B. G. J. (1991): Reply to comments by J. H. Bedard and R. S. J. Sparks, *Transactions of the Royal Society of Edinburgh: Earth Sciences*, **82**, pp. 391.

WADSWORTH, W. J. (1961): The layered ultrabasic rocks of south-west Rhum, Inner Hebrides, *Philosophical Transactions of the Royal Society, London*, **244B**, pp. 21-64.

WAGER, L. R. and BROWN, G. M. (1968): *Layered Igneous Rocks* (Edinburgh: Oliver and Boyd).

WAGER, L. R., BROWN, G. M. and WADSWORTH, W. J. (1960): Types of igneous cumulates, *Journal of Petrology*, **1**, pp. 73-85.

WICKHAM-JONES, C. R. and WOODMAN, P. C. (1998): Studies on the Earliest Settlement of Scotland and Ireland, *Quaternary International*, **49/50**, pp. 13-20.

WILLIAMS, C. T. (1985): Pyroclastic rocks in the Cnapan Breaca felsite, Rhum, *Geological Magazine*, **122**, pp. 447-50.

WILLIAMSON, I. T. and BELL, B. R. (1994): The Palaeocene lava field of west-central Skye, Scotland: stratigraphy, palaeogeography and structure, *Transactions of the Royal Society of Edinburgh: Earth Sciences*, **85**, pp. 39-75.

YOUNG, I. M. and DONALDSON, C. H. (1985): Formation of granular-textured layers and laminae within the Rhum crystal pile, *Geological Magazine*, **122**, pp. 519-28.

Key

(Key for figures 6, 10, 12, 19, 26, 33, 44, 45, 51, 58, 62 and 71. For scale, see kilometre grid. All heights are in feet.)

PALEOCENE

Canna Lava Formation (Post Rum Central Complex)

fW^H	Orval Member: hawaiite, basaltic hawaiite, commonly feldsparphyric
A^I	Guirdil Member: tholeiitic andesite
A^B	Upper Fionchra Member; basaltic andesite (fA^B, feldsparphyric basaltic andesite)
oB	Lower Fionchra Member: olivine-basalt, olivine-basaltic hawaiite
cg	Fluviatile conglomerate (interbedded with above)

Eigg Lava Formation (Pre-Rum Central Complex)

| B^B | Basalt (commonly crushed) |

RUM CENTRAL COMPLEX
Stage 2: (Layered Centre)

E^G	Gabbro and olivine-gabbro
byE^G	Bytownite-gabbro (Eucrite)
E^T	Bytownite-troctolite (Allivalite), E_I^T, where intrusive (includes gabbroic facies)
U	Peridotite and feldspathic peridotite
ΔU	Feldspathic peridotite breccias (ultrabasic inclusions in a feldspathic peridotite matrix)
▲U	Peridotite breccias (ultrabasic inclusions in a peridotite matrix)

Subscript letters and numbers against rocks in the Layered Centre:

Central Intrusion:
L, Long Loch member
R, Ruinsival member
D, Dornabac member

Western Layered Intrusion
A, Ard Mheall member
T, Transitional member
H, Harris Bay member

Eastern Layered Intrusion
1- 16, units of the layered sequence, numbered from 1 at the base.

Stage 1: Pre-Layered Centre: intrusive rocks

G	Microgranite, commonly granophyric FG where fine grained
R_i^R	Porphyritic rhyodacite, commonly flow-banded
X	Tuffisite, intrusive breccia
F^Gd	Microgranodiorite, quartz-microdiorite
I	Intrusion breccia (gabbro, dolerite and rare peridoite blocks in an intrusive microgranitic matrix)
▲ ▲ ▲	Am Màm Breccias (gneiss, gabbro and sandstone blocks in an intrusive microgranodioritic matrix)

Stage 1: Pre-Layered Centre: extrusive and sedimentary rocks

R_e^R	Porphyritic rhyodacite, commonly with eutaxitic texture
MBZ	Megabreccia (Torridon Group rock fragments up to 100m diameter
BZ	Coarse breccia, weakly bedded (subscript letters indicate the dominant clast type: L, Lewisian gneiss; T, Torridon Group sandstone; J, pale coloured Jurassic sandstone), sandstones commonly found at top of sequence (Epiclastic Sandstone), Z^SA

Other intrusive rocks of Paleocene age

U^P	Peridotite and feldspathic peridotite of plugs and dykes (U^D, dunite)
	Basalt and dolerite (D) dykes, sills and inclined sheets (fB, fD, feldsparphyric basalt or dolerite, B^P, D^P, picrite basalt or dolerite)
K	Unclassified basic sheets and dykes
hX	Fissure breccias
vR	Pitchstone dykes

148

MESOZOIC
LOWER JURASSIC

BFBsa	Sandstone
BFBls	Limestone
BFBsh	Mudstone

Broadford Beds

C	Calc-silicate rocks. Formed by thermal metamorphism of Lower Jurassic limestone during the Paleocene

TRIASSIC
Monadh Dubh Sandstone Formation

MODS	Sandstone, conglomerate and sedimentary breccia
MODS	Cornstone

PRECAMBRIAN
PROTEROZOIC (Torridon Group)

Aultbea Formation

TCSM	Sgor Mhòr Member: fine-grained sandstone, siltstone

Applecross Formation

TCAS	Scresort Sandstone Member: medium- and fine-grained sandstone with exotic pebbles
TCAM	Allt Mhòr na h-Uamha Member: interbedded fine-grained sandstone and siltstone

Diabaig Formation

TCDL	Laimhrig Shale Member: intercalated mudstone siltstone and fine-grained sandstone
TCDF	Fiachanis Gritty Sandstone Member: coarse-grained sandstone, local sedimentary breccias

ARCHEAN (Lewisian Gneiss Complex)

F	Feldspathic gneiss with amphibolite layers (commonly with Paleocene thermal metamorphic overprint)

Topographical Symbols

═══ Road	🪨 Cliff, flat rock and shingle
══ Track	‒²⁰⁰‒ Contour interval (25 ft)
‒ ‒ ‒ Path	
─── Old wall	◯ Loch
••••• Fence	◯ River
⊷⊷⊷ Pipeline	

OTHER FEATURES
Geological Symbols

⌐₁₈ Dip of strata, (in degrees)

⤢₁₅ Vertical strata

⤢²⁰ Dip of layering or flow-structures in intrusive igneous rocks and of welding foliation in extrusive igneous rocks, (in degrees)

⤙ Vertical layering, flow structures and welding foliation

⤡⁷⁰ Dip of foliation in gneiss, (in degrees)

⤙ Vertical foliation in gneiss

³⁵⟋ Dip of inclined basic sheets, (in degrees)

─── Geological boundary

------ Geological boundary where uncertain or gradual

━━ Fault

‒ ‒ ‒ Line of structural weakness

⊓⊓⊓ Benches and escarpments

Key based on *RUM – Solid Geology* (© Scottish Natural Heritage 1992).
Reproduced with the permission of the Scottish Natural Heritage. All rights reserved.

149

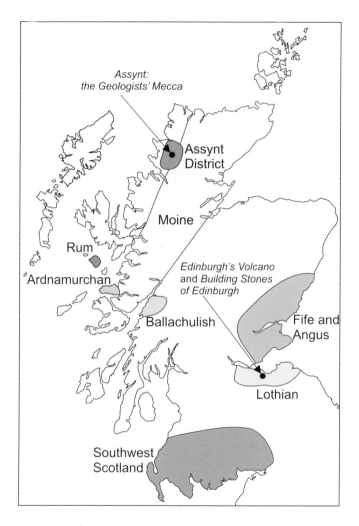

Map of Scotland showing the areas covered by
Excursion Guides of the Edinburgh Geological Society.
Leaflets are indicated in italics. For more information:

www.edinburghgeolsoc.org

1. 2nd edition of Moine to be published 2009; 2. SW Scotland is published jointly
with the British Geological Survey; 3. Fife and Angus is published by the Pentland Press
with financial support from the Society.